Tales of
Brother Marcus

Part One
The Rose Priory Dialogues

By
Allan Armstrong

IMAGIER PUBLISHING
Bristol 2009

First published in 2009 by:
Imagier Publishing
Rookery Farm
Bristol, BS35 3SY
United Kingdom
E-mail: ip@imagier.com
www.imagier.com

ISBN 13: 978-0-9558415-1-4

Cover and text design by Allan Armstrong
Cover image by Neil Murison RWA

Printed and bound in Great Britain by
CPI Antony Rowe, Eastbourne

Preface

One late afternoon last January, which was as cold and bitter a month as I can remember; everything was white with a frost that had been hanging around for days, and a thick bone-chilling fog smothered the country in a blanket of eerie silence. I was sitting at my desk examining the proofs of a book I was due to publish when a man appeared in my office. I say appeared because I didn't hear or see him enter. One moment I was alone, reading, then I looked up and there he was. He smiled and sat down in the chair clients generally used when visiting me and that was that.

Instead of asking him what he was doing in my office without an appointment, which I would have normally done, as I don't like cold calls, I asked him how I could help him. In response he produced a handwritten manuscript and asked me to read it, and if I liked it to publish it. He said his name was Joseph and that he was the author. I opened the manuscript and began to read. After a few minutes I looked up to ask him a question and he had gone; disappeared if you like. Thus began a peculiar relationship in which Joseph appeared in my office without me ever seeing him arrive and where he left without me ever seeing him leave.

Table of Contents

Part One

A Remarkable Encounter

I first met the old monk in the autumn of 1981. A work colleague invited me to a meeting of people interested in the esoteric. I had agreed to go but without expecting much from it. The truth was I was quite worn-out and too tired to get excited about anything, because for the last five years, and with no great success, I'd been wandering the world looking for genuine exponents of the mystical life. I had not long since returned from a fascinating but fruitless visit to India, where I had spent the best part of a year looking for an Indian holy man. Sadly all I came across were a host of weird and wonderful people, interesting in many ways, but none of them proving to be the real thing. I met quite a few who laid claim to the title, but in the end they proved to be either mad, deluded, or just sharp 'business-gurus' looking to make money from gullible Europeans and Americans.

I know India has more than its fair share of spiritual masters, but I didn't find any, although there was one man, a Shiva-baba, who was certainly committed to his path and not particularly interested in my money, but at the time I thought he was still a journeyman developing his skills. I guess by now, some twenty year later, if he is still alive, he's probably a master of his discipline. One thing I did encounter, however, and with a vengeance, was dysentery and without the assistance of a traditional Indian doctor I would surely have died. Thus I returned to England in the spring of 1981, exhausted, penniless and almost completely disillusioned. I needed time to recuperate, somewhere to live and a job to earn some money so, after spending a few weeks being cosseted by my parents, I took a job driving a van for an antiques shipper, and found a room in a shared house. The room was adequate for my needs – better than anything I had in India – and the people I shared the house with were pleasant enough. As an added bonus the job not only paid enough to live on but also allowed me to save a little money each month. Which brings me to the point. It was at work, that I met Leo, another driver, who to my amazement was as interested as I in all things mystical, and it was he who invited me to a weekly meeting of people interested in the 'esoteric' run by an old monk, Brother Marcus. To be honest I was sceptical about the outcome.

Now you should know that in my youth mysticism was invariably associated with Hinduism or Buddhism; indeed popular opinion then, just like today, perceived spiritual disciplines such as meditation to be connected only with oriental religions and philosophies. Indeed, the archetypal images that presented themselves to my young imagination were those of a Buddhist monk or Indian sadhu sitting cross-legged on a cushion or low wooden stool, eyes closed and breathing slowly, invariably chanting. However, as real and romantic as such visions might be, it is difficult to find them being realised in the environs of modern

A Remarkable Encounter

industrialised cities; which is the reason why I went looking outside Europe in the first place. So, apart from knowing that it wasn't Indian or Buddhist, I had no idea what to expect from this meeting.

My dad had given me some money and I'd bought a car, an old but well cared for Morris Traveller. It was advertised in the window of the local post-office. I bought it from a retired teacher who'd lost the sight of one eye and was on the way to losing the sight in the other. She could no longer drive and had reluctantly put her car up for sale. It was green and smelled strongly of lavender, which I rather liked; it reminded me of my grandparents' house whose wooden floors were polished with lavender beeswax. Anyway, it was agreed that I should meet Leo and his girlfriend Louise at the Atlantis café, and travel to the Rose Priory in my car.

The Atlantis café was a favourite meeting place for people interested in the esoteric. It lay at the heart of the old part of town. Many of the buildings dated back to the seventeenth century, although more than a few were much earlier. In this area were to be found art galleries and specialist shops selling antiques, second-hand books and the like. Also in this district could be found dealers in all things esoteric and supernatural, from rare alchemical manuscripts and objets d'art to the most recent offerings of the 'New-Age' movement. I remember paying a few shillings for a first edition of Tolkein's *Lord of the Rings,* reading it and giving it to a casual acquaintance; its scarcity meant little to me and none of the people I knew then had any interest in 'first editions' unless they were really old. Many books and manuscripts, now impossible to find, seemed reasonably accessible then, indeed there was no sense that such objects would become so valuable. Anyway, the Atlantis café was my favourite meeting place on Saturdays, particularly when searching for old books on esoteric subjects. Sadly the area has since become 'fashionable' and most of the interesting shops have long since been replaced by interior designers, computer shops and estate agents.

We set off for the Priory, some eight or nine miles out of the city. It nestled in a shallow valley between the beach and an ancient woodland. A long sloping meadow separated the house from the woodland, and my first impression was one of peace and tranquillity. It was an old country house, a rambling three storey building, built in the eighteenth century, with no pretensions whatsoever towards architectural greatness, although it was pretty enough to look at in a plain sort of way. Its irregular stone walls had long since been painted cream or magnolia and the stone flagged roof had signs of moss on it, but the most interesting feature was the arched front door, which looked really ancient. It was made of vertical wooden planks with metal studs, probably iron, set into an arched stone doorframe. Over the succeeding weeks I discovered that the Rose Priory had many puzzling features which only began to make sense when I realised that it had been rebuilt several times over the centuries, with many existing materials cannibalised in the rebuild.

As we walked form the car I could hear, very faintly, the sound of people chanting. At first I thought it was a recording

A Remarkable Encounter

but then I realised that it was real; it sounded as if it wa:
from the other side of the building, which it was, as ı later
discovered. I realised then that I was entering a religious house –
this was the real deal, not a fantasy. Somewhere deep within me I
recalled the fact that the ancient sound of monks chanting in
Plainsong had alway touched the core of my being; it felt like I was
returning home, wherever that might be. The truth is I don't
understand why, but I know, and in no rational way, that I connect
with Plainsong, particularly Gregorian chant, far more than with
any other musical sound; so by the time we arrived at the door I
was already feeling uplifted with a smile in my heart. The front
door was opened by what appeared to be the oldest man in the
world. He wasn't very tall and completely bald. His gaunt face was
deeply etched with lines and his soft smiling eyes penetrated right
through me. He looked ancient but not haggard; indeed, beneath
his black robe, a robe tied at the waist with a white cord, there
appeared to be the outline of a solid and upright body. He said not a
word, just nodded and smiled serenely as we entered following
closely behind a young couple.

The interior of the Priory was far more interesting than the
exterior. The floorboards looked as if they were medieval, and
probably were; they had obviously been lovingly polished over
many years, and the smell of beeswax permeated the air. We
followed the couple through a door on the left and found ourselves
in a large half-panelled room. On the floor lay a large oriental
carpet, made up of many colours, all faded with age, although red
was the most dominant colour. The wall panels looked as though
they came from an old church – which I later discovered was the

case, along with the floor. Through one of the windows the coast of Wales, veiled in mist, beckoned enchantingly. Over the next few months I learnt that a religious building had stood here for more than a thousand years, and that the same religious Order had owned it for most of that time, and I heard rumours that an extensive warren of caves and tunnels lay beneath the Priory, but no-one really knew anything about it.

The gathering was not large, some fifteen or sixteen people as I recall. Tea, coffee, fruitcake and biscuits were being served, and almost everyone smoked. It was very bizarre to say the least. In my travels, particularly in Europe and America, the norm for such gatherings is strictly no smoking, and if refreshments were offered they were generally vegetarian if not vegan, and certainly no tea or coffee. Indeed, smoking and smokers were thoroughly frowned upon if not scorned for displaying such obvious signs of weakness and spiritual degeneration. Furthermore, any person committing such a crime would probably be asked to leave and told not to come back, not even to apologise; an occurrence I'd witnessed on more than one occasion over the last few years. Yet, here it didn't seem to matter what anyone did, and the atmosphere was very friendly.

Everyone was gathered in this spacious room which seemed to be either a very large study or a communal library. It was lined with books occasionally interspersed with paintings, mostly by the early twentieth century artists, although some of them looked like much older religious paintings. An old oak trestle table, which must have been twelve feet long, stood at one end of the room set with refreshments. At the other end a small but cheery fire crackled in a large stone fireplace. The fireplace was surrounded by old and jaded easy chairs of many different styles and sizes. Here people gathered, some sitting, some standing, all engaged in private conversations with someone or other.

In an old cane chair sat a man whose age could have been anywhere between fifty and eighty. He wore his white hair and equally white beard close cropped; it had thinned from the front giving him a pronounced forehead. He seemed to be of medium height and build, dressed in a black robe, a cassock, as it turned out. Upon his head he wore a dark red skullcap and around his neck hung a cross, made of gold or brass – whatever the material the cross was hand-made – a little crude but pleasing to look at. On his feet were red socks and black sandals. Other than the cross, a gold signet ring set with a deep purple stone was the only jewellery he wore, unless one counted a chaplet of dark brown wooden beads hung loosely around the wrist of his right hand.

An old clock standing in the corner chimed eight o'clock and everyone in the room gradually fell silent and stood up. The old man, who was obviously Brother Marcus, speaking with an accent difficult to place, but probably northern, asked everyone to be still, and then after a moment's silence commenced the meeting with a prayer, after which everyone sat down. As he uttered the prayer, the atmosphere gradually but noticeably changed, It became so still I could have touched it with my finger, if I had dared move; and there was an air of expectancy that made my skin tingle.

He took a sip from his cup and looked at the people gathered around him, particularly those he had not seen before, myself included. He composed himself and spoke: "Welcome to the Rose

The Rose Priory Dialogues

Priory. For some of you this is your first visit, others have been here before. For the benefit of those who are new my name is Brother Marcus. I am the Prior of the Order of St. Denys; a religious order dedicated to the contemplative life. This Order was established more than a hundred years ago for men and women who live in the world yet wish to dedicate themselves to the spiritual life. These meetings are held every week to discuss that life. No subject is excluded, unless it is obviously irrelevant or unseemly, and other than good manners and tolerance there are no expectations. The Order does not actively seek members nor does it look to separate you from your money. If there is an agenda it is simply to share in the spiritual life. Some people discover that what we do here is not to their liking or taste, and stop coming, others enjoy the meetings and continue to attend. On these terms all are welcome." Marcus smiled and sat down. "Oh by the way, there is no specific curriculum or agenda; if you have any questions or anything to say then do speak out."

I was thinking about what a contemplative Order was; I'd heard the term before but had never really understood it, when I heard myself say, "What is a contemplative Order?" "Interesting question", he replied. "The best way I can describe it is as a community of people dedicated to prayer and meditation. In secular terms the word 'contemplation' means to think deeply but in spiritual terms it has another very different meaning that is only truly understood by those who engage with it. The clearest illustration I can give you at this time is that of the deep states of meditation often attributed to eastern and oriental mystics, but also central to the Christian way of life from the very beginning;

indeed, the Order was established to assist people to engage in such work." His last few words intrigued me. I tried to grasp the significance of them. He was saying something I intuitively knew to be right yet had never really thought about before. Who today would think of a Christian being mystical? Yet, as I realised later, it is blindingly obvious to any who might consider the matter that the spiritual path was a fundamental part of primitive Christianity, but how few of my generation could see, or indeed actually wanted to see it. I really wanted to engage with him on this subject, but I found myself tongue-tied, so many questions flooded my mind that all I could do was smile and mutter an inane "Thank you".

Marcus smiled, his eyes revealing nothing, he just looked right into my mind, holding me in some kind of trance. I think I might well have fallen over if he hadn't resumed speaking; "Are you at peace with yourself?" For a brief moment I thought he was talking to me, but quickly realised that he was addressing everyone in the room. "I doubt it", he continued; "few people are at peace with themselves or free from fear, yet you can be you know; although money can't buy it, nor can anyone give it to you. Indeed, there is no magic wand or bottle of medicine, or laying on of hands by 'elevated souls' that will give you true peace of mind or freedom from fear. It is only by entering into the depth of your own soul, following the path of self-knowledge, that these things may be attained, and then only by your own efforts.

However, it is possible to be guided along that path, but don't make the mistake of giving another person the responsibility for your own spiritual awakening, no matter how adept and 'spiritual' they may seem to be. In this work a teacher can do no more than guide you, the rest is in your hands and your hands alone; and the results will be determined by how much you engage with the work and the disciplines involved. So, if you are all agreeable I will describe a few of the principles that I was introduced to when I joined the Order; they may be of interest to you. I was instructed that these simple precepts are the foundations upon which any philosophical or spiritual system is built; and that they are applicable to any teacher and teaching in the world. They are quite universal and not too difficult to understand."

Everyone in the room signalled or vocalised their consent, and Marcus continued. "The first principle I was introduced to is the principle of Tolerance. In this work it is essential as every person you will meet on the way will have their own opinions and beliefs, many of which will differ quite radically from your own, and whilst you don't have to change your life to suit others, you will find that it will be enhanced if you develop the attitude of mind that every one has a right to their own ideas, that they are right from their own point of view and level of understanding. That somone else's views differ from your own simply means that in practical terms both of you believe yourselves to be right – even though your rightness might not be theirs. For example, some people are atheists, others believe in God. Although they may have contradictory points of view those who follow this path accept both as being entitled to their views, recognising that in due course everyone will arrive at the truth. Put another way, just because religious and cultural intolerance is endemic in this world it doesn't mean we must follow the herd, even if we have been brought up to do so. As a novice, tolerance was the first, and easily

A Remarkable Encounter

the most difficult lesson I had to learn. It was summed up in the words; 'If you are to follow in the footsteps of the Lord, then learn to love all creatures equally.' I must say that I am still learning that lesson, as you will undoubtedly find out. It is the first important lesson you will encounter, and probably the last that you will truly understand."

A young man called Gregory interrupted Marcus, "You seem to be suggesting that we should accept any and every point of view. How does this fit with extreme belief systems that are typical of religious fundamentalism or radical political thinking for instance. There's a lot to choose from, I'm thinking of extreme right wing political organisations that could easily radicalise our society, but the same doubts apply to various cults that given a foothold would do the same. Don't we have a personal responsibility for our freedom?" "Of course" replied Marcus, "but do you believe that the force of your convictions will change the views of the members of such organisations; I'm not so sure they will. That they exist suggests that either from the strength of their arguments or through the absence of any other, people have given their allegiance to such organisations. If you choose to ignore them, to not engage with them, or to make their existence illegal, you only radicalise them and give them strength. Is this not so?" Gregory didn't answer immediately; he chewed his bottom lip nervously whilst looking for a response. After a moment he said, "I understand what you say, I know it is a thorny issue, but at what point does tolerance become weakness?"

Marcus responded, "Perhaps the answer lies in accepting that the existence of other opinions does not necessarily undermine our own. For example, I'm a Christian, however, from my perspective it is not important whether Christianity is or is not a superior way to other religious systems. For many reasons it is the most appropriate path for me to follow. If I'd been born a Hindu I would in all probability have followed one of the religious systems of Hinduism. I see many parallels between Christianity and Hinduism, but then I also see many differences. Furthermore, although I can see great dangers in Fascism I can also see that the political and social objectives of Fascism are rooted in a perceived need for a strong social identity. I don't have to agree with the radical views expressed by many of its exponents to recognise that such a need exists. Arguably, such organisations come into being because the needs they satisfy are not provided for elsewhere; that is not because of the weakness inherent in tolerance, quite possibly the opposite. There are countless points of view about such things, but, Gregory, is it not more important that we examine and understand our own prejudices than condemn the prejudices of other people. Remember these principles are intended to help souls on their spiritual journey; they are not intended to be a complete political system, they never were." I think the penny dropped for Gregory, because he responded to Marcus's words by saying, quite gently, "I guess everything has to be seen in context, I think I was missing the point you were making. Thank you, Marcus."

Marcus continued, "Another principle fundamental to this work was described to me as Right Thinking, which is simply thinking that which you know to be right. However, be warned, it can be a little bit tricky because certainty based on truth and reality

A Remarkable Encounter

is a rare thing. It was pointed out to me by my teacher that, even though we take many things for granted, there is little in life we can truly be certain about, thus right thinking is something that can't be forced but will evolve as we proceed on our journey through life. Opportunities, on the other hand, will arise whereby we will discover other ways of thinking that are of a superior nature to those we currently adopt; and so our current 'right thinking' will modify. This process of mental modification is not to be feared but welcomed.

Our present way of thinking is conditioned by our environment and cultural upbringing. From the moment we were born we have been influenced by our environment, by the culture we were born into, by our family, even by the climate. Let me give you a personal example. I was brought up in a family that never drank coffee or wine. I was a teenager before I drank my first cup of coffee, and I was in my early twenties when I drank my first glass of wine. Everybody in the neighbourhood smoked, including, I suspect, the dog. Culture was based around the pub, the radio and eventually the television.

Most of my generation were expected to follow our parents, working in the mines or the shipyards. Alternatively some became tradesmen, others joined the Merchant Navy or the Armed Forces; a few became teachers, but not many, whilst a tiny minority made it to university. Public opinion was formed by the tabloids and the Radio/TV. Life expectations were clearly laid out. If we were industrious we would secure a job, marry, live in a council house, raise a family and retire at the age of sixty-five. Holidays would be taken in local seaside resorts. Acceptable behaviour and right thinking was established in the context of such norms. People who behaved outside of the norm were viewed as being different and sometimes with suspicion. I suspect that it is as true today as it was then. However, just because people with different conditioning and experiences will have different ideas about what constitutes right thinking, there is no need to enter into conflict with them or yourself over such differences, just accept that different ideas exist on the subject, instead of looking for an argument or a validation of your own views. Simply enjoy the fact that these differences exist, it can only enhance your understanding of the concept of tolerance. Furthermore, you will be more likely to notice your own ideas changing as you go through life; indeed, habitual thought patterns that once seemed like prison bars will dissolve as new ways of thinking take their place. There is no need for a degree in philosophy or psychology to be proficient in right thinking. On the other hand, it is not something we take out of a box ready to use, but something we grow into as we develop."

"I'm sorry to be so contentious", interrupted Gregory, "but how do I engage with the principle of right thinking when I'm not really sure about anything, I mean how is anyone to judge whether or not they are misguided or really applying this principle in their lives?" "We have to take a position, a view, if you like," replied Marcus. "We must examine our beliefs, to see them for what they are in the context of our experience and understanding. For most of us it will involve talking to and questioning our elders, seeking guidance from those we respect the most. In following such a path we will not only learn a great deal, but occasionally we will be disappointed as contradictions and paradoxes arise that will confuse us; nevertheless, we have to make a stand, and whatever form that stand takes, it will be for each of us the place from which we begin our journey; I was driven to find the common ground in all religions – because I believed then, and continue to believe now, that the finest expressions of human endeavour are contained therein.

One thing is certain about that beginning, each of us will start from a place of spiritual darkness, from which we will move gradually towards a place of light and understanding. We might rush, we might dawdle, and occasionally we will push ourselves beyond our limited understanding, taking many wrong turnings in the process, but we will begin. However, when we begin depends upon when we are ready. It is written 'Many are called', suggesting that we are indeed prompted, but, it is an inner prompting that is incomprehensible to those who have not felt it. Once a soul feels the prompting it can do nothing else but begin the journey; and, Gregory, you may recall that I said these principles were intended to help souls on their spiritual journey, well it is such souls who have felt the prompting I had in mind.

Many struggle to understand what is happening to them, some undertake extreme disciplines and put themselves through harsh regimes, under the misguided belief that any form of asceticism will do. However, as a novice I was constantly reminded by my teacher that it is not necessary to put myself under pressure because spiritual development cannot be forced, it emerges slowly like a flower. It begins with a need to understand who and what we are in the context of this wonderfully mysterious universe; indeed the beginning of this journey is an adventure in

The Rose Priory Dialogues

Self-knowledge, and whether you are sure or unsure is immaterial, that you are called or not called is everything. I don't expect you to understand my answer at this point, but one day you will." Gregory said nothing, but slumped back in his chair.

He tried to look nonchalant but I could see that he was crimson with embarrassment, almost as if Marcus had shamed him. It occurred to me at the time that his disposition was going to make his integration within the group here somewhat difficult. Marcus decided that a break was called for and left the room. A few went outside to smoke a cigarette; others found refreshments and stood around in small groups chatting. I could see Gregory in an animated discussion with Leo and moved closer to hear what they were talking about. As I negotiated my way through the small huddles of people my way was blocked by a slender middle-aged woman with an amazing head of red hair. I mumbled hello, and informed her that this was my first visit. She said her name was Jenny and that she had attended several of these meetings and found them fascinating. I wasn't sure what to say so I asked her what she did for a day job. She told me that she was a psychotherapist, and then asked me if I understood or had ever felt the prompting that Marcus had spoken about. Her question, even though it was too close to the bone for me to answer, was strangely inoffensive. I mumbled something about it being difficult to say one way or another, which oddly enough echoed her own position, but although I was in reality being evasive, her words clarified something for me. I had been prompted, I knew that, and it hadn't made me feel very happy, the truth was I had felt wretched for years, and my journeys in search of a true exponent of the spiritual

A Remarkable Encounter

life who might help me understand it were driven by it. This was, I believe, the first time I had consciously admitted it to myself, and I suspect I was being driven towards Gregory to talk about it because I could see something in him that echoed what was going on in my own mind. Anyway, by the time the opportunity arose for me to speak with him he had gone, because Marcus re-entered the room and signalled by rattling his cup with a spoon that we should continue.

He sat quietly for a minute then said, "Try to understand that the spiritual path is a path of developing and evolving an understanding of self through working with our own nature rather than trying to overcome it with force. My teacher showed me how to observe the universe around me, both 'within' and 'without'; to recognise what a wonderful creation it is, a creation made by a God worthy of being celebrated and worshipped, certainly not an inept deity who made mistakes or got it wrong. He taught me to understand that everything in the world is in its right and proper place; and that it is we, the spiritually naïve, who do not understand the unfolding wonder that is creation. He said that our current understanding is based upon past experience, which in itself conditions our thoughts, and that we should cultivate right thinking as it leads us away from conditioned thinking and has the capacity to lift us up to the highest levels of thought, where it is possible to comprehend that which is perfect within us. And no matter how great the struggle or how many times we might fail to keep up with it, it will always be there; so, rather than expecting the highest level of achievement in right thinking at the outset, simply be true to your own understanding of the principle – let it grow in you rather than you growing in it – it is not a race.

"The third principle is the principle of Right Action. It is a fundamental part of the teaching that thought affects change in the body. In fact it is difficult if not impossible to think of anything without the thought having an effect on the body in one way or another; it might be a muscular contraction, a glandular secretion, or a chemical change. Indeed, whatever the response, be assured that every thought will affect the body and influence subsequent actions, from which we may deduce that from thinking comes action and from right thinking emerges right action. Therefore do try and work with the idea that every action is the result of thinking. However, be warned, a given action may not be an immediate or obvious response to a current thought; it could just as well be a response to a thought that has been sitting for some time, as it were, in the back of your mind. My teacher explained it this way. He suggested that the mind responds to stimuli by drawing on a precedent or memory to supply an appropriate reaction. If a direct fit is not available then it will search for a related action – a next best fit. He further explained that should the mind be unable to find a suitable reaction it would be inclined to become temporarily neurotic, displaying signs of its inability to cope such as irritability, hunger etc., a bit like a dog not being able to deal with a situation sitting down and scratching itself as an act of "doing something about it". His point was that because how a person thinks determines their actions then memories become seeds for future events and behaviour. Therefore, we should look to see the good in everything and everybody, to think at the highest level we are capable of, filling our mind as best we can with spiritual thoughts, because those who think right will act right. This, he taught, is a principle that lies at the heart of rectifying our life because as we learn how specific behaviours have specific consequences we learn how to modify our behaviour and thereby modify the consequences. In short, if we modify our thinking we modify our actions, and consequently modify the outcome of our life.

"It is from the third principle that the fourth principle derives, that we are the sum total of our memory. Memory can be divided into two parts: that which enters through the conscious mind, and that which enters through subconscious avenues. For the sake of this discussion I shall refer to the first part as Memory because it can be recalled through the conscious mind, and the second part I shall refer to as Records, which are memories stored in the subconscious mind, and to which we usually do not have immediate access; these are far more extensive than we usually imagine. For example, think of the last person you met, you may remember what that person's name was, and what he or she might have looked like, and possibly what you discussed, but the subconscious mind has recorded all the information available to the senses during this meeting, including the minutiae of the environment, and everything in it. You might remember the most pertinent things but the recording part of the mind misses nothing.

"These recordings can and do associate with each other, and the power of recall is based upon the chemistry of such associations. Another factor to understand is that each part of a record is of the same value. An appropriate analogy would be an audio recording, where every sound is faithfully picked up by the microphone and recorded, there is no discrimination or rejection, all of it goes into the recording. So does everything that happens within the scope of our senses, it is all recorded with equal value. Although we may not have ready access to it, the recording part of our mind cannot forget anything that it has recorded. However, under certain conditions, such as in hypnosis, these records can be brought into the conscious mind. Thus, the implications point to the necessity of forming good memories, because, every good thing we do is the direct result of the good that we have thought; so, be careful what you think.

The fifth principle proposes that you think of yourself as a triad consisting of three integrated parts; the conscious self, the subconscious self, and the Divine Self. The first two parts we've touched upon, and to some degree you may well be able to formulate an image or concept of them, but the latter part, the Divine Self will be more difficult. There are many names and titles associated with it: The Breath of God, The Unborn One, The Deathless One, the Ruach, the Atman, and probably the most common – The Lord. Personally, I prefer the term 'Lord', but whatever name is used it describes and applies to that part of the triad which comes from God, clothed in a cloak of skin. He is the essential "I Am" within our soul, and we should note that on this premise all mysticism stands.

"There is a meditation technique that has long been used for developing spiritual thoughts and memories. It is based upon selecting a verse from the scriptures and thinking about its significance. The main focus of the technique rests on emphasising

A Remarkable Encounter

different words, for example, a line from Psalm 27 states; "The Lord is my light and salvation". If the emphasis is placed upon "The *Lord* is my light and salvation", we may reflect upon the question who is the Lord that is referred to here. Using the idea of the Triad as a key it is possible to think of the Lord as the Divine Self within the soul. It is the part of us that is deathless and immortal; the Lord of our life. If the emphasis is placed upon the words; "*is my light*", then it is possible to understand that the Lord, of whom we have little knowledge or understanding is the light of our life, a constant, present, and personal essence, not an impersonal detached abstraction. In using this technique any thoughts that arise should be kept in the forefront of the mind until the idea has been imprinted in the recording mind. This simple discipline forms the basis for developing good memories and you should take your time in studying it because the implications are very profound, and what is more, only good can come from such work.

"Another exercise is called Selective Thinking; it is in many ways the real beginning of meditation. It is the practice of choosing a subject to occupy your mind on command, in an instant. Many people find this exercise a little difficult at first, but practice makes it easier. You may find your mind wandering from the subject, but don't worry, just gently bring the subject back again, and again if necessary. Make one of the themes of selective thinking be the affirmation: "I have the power and control to think those things I wish to think". Make it a positive desire to gain control of selective thinking so that you can give your whole mind to any subject you desire. A small notebook can be used to enter any ideas or themes that you have decided to think about. It has been my experience that when meditation is mentioned there is generally some confusion about what it is. Many people are inclined to think that meditation is sitting in the silence concentrating upon the ebb and flow of the breath or perhaps engaging in some creative imagination. Such things may well be part of it, but few grasp the simple truth that meditation is simply mind control, and selective thinking is the first step in achieving that control. A variation of this method consists of writing down any pertinent thoughts or images that emerge in the mind; the tip of the pen becomes the single point of awareness and expression. There are many such methods available, indeed, at different times one method may be more suitable than another.

The sixth principle proposes that the universe is created by God and is therefore perfect. It is a difficult notion to reconcile with the suffering and madness we see taking place in the world. Yet for the contemplative, to say that God is perfect is to state the obvious because 'God' is perfect by definition. Therefore, to say that Creation is perfect is equally true because it is inconceivable that imperfection may come out of perfection. However, given the diverse nature of human experience it is inevitable that the idea of God's perfection should be challenged, thus questions arise. The following is a classic example: Can a God who is perfect act in an imperfect manner? This question gives rise to a paradox because if the answer is no, then the omnipotence of God is limited and therefore imperfect, and if the answer is yes, then the integrity of God's perfection is questionable. It would appear that God cannot win either way. In reality the question is typical of human thought and speculation creating a god in its own limited image and then creating specious arguments against it. In this example God seems to be in a no win situation – or would be if limited by human understanding, but the argument is a human argument with human terms and limitations, and the answer, well, it is not to be found in questioning the motives and integrity of God, but in questioning the nature of human expectations from existence.

It is obvious that humanity's understanding of life at this stage in its development is seriously limited. Factors such as life expectancy, ageing, social conditioning, technology and learning ability etc. are as yet insufficiently developed for an accurate perspective of reality. So it is not surprising that a great deal still perplexes us; senseless acts of barbarism and savagery, and seemingly meaningless afflictions of disease upon the young and defenceless, anger and bewilder us because our limited powers of understanding are incapable of realising the true significance of such events. However, the lessons of experience will eventually teach us that we will be far better served forming our humanity in God's image by transforming our vices into virtues, and dropping the pursuit of self-interest in favour of the common good. Only then perhaps, will the conditions that are universally abhorred, yet often our own creations, become obsolete as the divine potential within humanity is more fully expressed.

This is more or less the situation described in the Hindu classic, the Bhagavad Gita, which on the surface appears to be an ancient Hindu story of a dialogue between the god Krishna and the prince Arjuna, a prince who is about to engage in a battle between different factions of his people. The story begins by informing us that Arjuna was in a great turmoil about the moral implications of the impending battle, a battle between friends and relatives. Krishna appears and a great dialogue begins. However, the story is far more than a moral tale; there is embedded in the Bhagavad Gita a spiritual teaching concerning the evolution of the soul; the essence of which requires that we see Arjuna as a metaphor of the aspiring part of our self. It is expected that we should try to identify with him, to see him as the part of our self that is seeking to overcome the negative aspects of the world in order to attain union with God. Like Arjuna we are surrounded by a continually shifting sea of conflict and suffering, how do we deal with it. Do we seek to resolve it with an undeveloped intellect and inadequate understanding, or do we, like Arjuna, seek inspiration from the divine spark that resides within? By turning to the indwelling Godhead, seeking the good in all things we may also, like Arjuna, be overcome with wonder as we realise that it is God's universe that is all around us, and that we are active participants in that universe."

Sitting by the fire, eyes closed in concentration, I had been transfixed by Marcus's words, so much so that I failed to notice that he had stopped talking and left his seat. By the time I had gathered my wits he was over by the main table pouring himself a cup of coffee. Several conversations sprang up between different people and by the time Marcus returned to his seat the room was bubbling with the sound of quiet voices engaged in earnest discussion. He didn't seem inclined to resume speaking, instead he simply leaned back in his chair and relaxed, enjoying his coffee. And so the rest of the evening passed in a state of blissful

A Remarkable Encounter

tranquillity and brother Marcus basked in the warmth of its atmosphere. Somewhere between eleven and midnight the discussions gradually wound down. Marcus called everyone together and closed the meeting with a prayer, and we all went home, A different member of the Order, a much younger man, tall and thin, sporting a wispy beard, stood by the door and bade us goodnight. I drove back in silence, thinking about my remarkable encounter with this intriguing man; he surely wasn't a typical Christian monk, or was he? Leo and Louise were equally quiet and I dropped them off on the way home. I didn't sleep much that night but sat by the gas fire thinking about this strange old monastic and how in discussing the subject of being called or not, he put his finger right on the most sensitive part of my soul. I looked forward to meeting him again.

Part Two

Metaphors & Meditation

The following week the weather was dreadful, indeed the whole week was one grey wet and cold mess. For the first time since I returned I pined for the sultry heat of India, so much so that on several occasions the smell of Indian spices filled my mind; in truth it was so strong there were times when I swear I could physically smell the food stalls and hear the perpetual noise and chatter of India's teeming streets. I ate a lot of Indian food that week.

Work was hectic. I seemed to be forever driving up and down motorways collecting and delivering furniture to and from various auction rooms and shipping warehouses. I didn't see Leo to speak with for any length of time, other than to arrange picking him up on Friday; nor did I see anyone else connected with the Rose Priory all week, so when Friday evening arrived I was ready for it. I managed to get away early and took the opportunity to eat at the Atlantis Café. I arrived at the café about five o'clock and took a seat by the window, where I could look out onto the grey, wet and noisy cityscape. I ordered a lasagne with salad and settled down to read the paper and savour a decent cup of coffee.

The Rose Priory Dialogues

I hadn't been sitting more than five minutes when a voice said, "Do I really want to sit next to a man reading a tabloid full of erotic images?" I looked up, into the eyes of a vivacious redhead. I knew I'd met her before, but for the life of me I just could not remember where. "This is the *Times*, madam, it does not do erotic pictures, it wouldn't know how." I said feigning an offended dignity in the deepest and most serious tone I could muster. "But seriously, you have me at a disadvantage; I know we've met, but...?" "At the Rose Priory", she quickly interrupted me, "We met last week, do you remember now?" "Of course," I said, full of relief, "You're Jenny, aren't you?" "You remembered my name, how delightful," she had a very attractive voice. "I thought I would eat here before I went on to the Priory, are you going tonight?" she said. "Yes, of course," I replied, "I'm here on the same mission as yourself. I finished work early and thought it a good idea to eat before the meeting. I'm also meeting up with Leo, and his girlfriend, Louise, we're going to the Priory in my car." "Splendid," said Jenny, "We can enjoy a meal together, far more entertaining than eating alone, what you are having?" "Lasagne", I replied, "With salad". "What a good choice, I am very envious you know, unfortunately I'm on a diet, no wheat or dairy for the next two months, so I'll have to eat something simple." She uttered those words with a deep sigh of regret. I held back from asking why she was on such a diet, I wasn't sure I could deal with the answer, so without saying a word I handed her the menu, folded the paper and put it away.

Jenny looked at the menu, went to the counter, ordered something or other then rejoined me. She seemed to be bothered by something, but was hiding it reasonably well. "What do you think of the Priory", she said softly. "Really interesting, I particularly like Brother Marcus. Why do you ask?" "Oh, no reason really, I feel much like you do, it's just that I don't know anybody there, I feel a bit like a stranger at a family wedding, if you know what I mean?" "Perhaps", I replied. "On the other hand, perhaps everyone there is in the same boat, strangers in a strange land. I've only been once before myself, and I was introduced by Leo, you might have noticed him last week; he's the one who was juggling with bean bags – he went to a school for clowns, I think." "Oh, what fun she exclaimed", she seemed truly excited at the prospect of doing the same. "I think I know who you mean, but no, I don't know him." Our food arrived and we sat eating in silence for a moment. "You told me last week that you were a psychotherapist; what do you specialise in?" I asked. "Oh, mostly confidence boosting and loneliness counselling," she replied, "but I'm far more interested in knowing something about my own soul, it is such a mystery. Peel away a layer and another appears before your very eyes. Marcus interests me because he has a way of reaching past the layers. I hope to learn a lot from him. If I have a reservation about him it is that I'm afraid that he'll turn out to be a fake, just like so many I've come across." I understood what was bothering her now; her reservation was a genuine concern that she might be conned. The truth is we have only so much hope in us and having it continually trashed is indescribably painful. I was just about to answer her when Leo and his girlfriend entered the café.

When we arrived at the Priory there were some twenty people present at the meeting. Everyone seemed to be enjoying the warmth and the glow of the fire. The meeting began precisely at eight o'clock. As before it began with an evocative prayer that seemed to encompass all of us in an atmosphere of peace. Marcus began the meeting by asking if anyone had any suggestions for discussion. A man in his mid-thirties spoke out, his refined Scandinavian accent resonating around the room: "last week you said many spiritual texts were written using allegories and metaphors. I'm hoping that you'll expand on that subject this evening; that is if everyone is o.k. about it." Most nodded in agreement and a few voiced their approval of the subject. Marcus closed his eyes, for a moment looking within; then looked up and said: "A marvellous choice, Erik, and a subject difficult to exhaust, but first let me ask you all a question, what is an allegory and what is a metaphor?" A young Kenyan woman, whose name I later found out was Ruth, spoke out: "As I understand it the word 'allegory' suggests the use of a narrative to explain or give greater meaning to a perplexing story or a puzzle. Whereas the term 'metaphor' is more symbolic, it involves using a word or an expression in place of something else, for example; 'it's a pain in the neck', is a metaphor for something that is troublesome, or 'to cast your bread on the waters', is a metaphor for taking a risk, and a story about someone taking a risk would be an allegory." I thought Ruth was going to continue but she seemed to think better of it and fell silent. No-one seemed prepared to add to her definition so Marcus spoke: "Thank you Ruth, that's as good a definition as any, and it serves our purpose well, because it is important for us to comprehend the distinction between them if we are ever to understand the subject."

Metaphors & Meditation

Marcus fell silent for a moment, the crackling fire and the ticking of the old clock were the only sounds in the room as everyone focussed on their own thoughts. After a minute or so, although it seemed to me that time had lost all sense of meaning and it could easily have been an hour, Marcus said: "Christ often used allegorical tales called parables as a means of teaching people. The phrase: 'The kingdom of heaven is like unto...' is often used by the Lord to introduce the listener to something that cannot be touched or seen with the physical senses, but may be perceived with the mind if it is attuned correctly, and parables enable us to do just that; moreover, occasionally they can turn into metaphors, for example, the story of the wedding feast at Canaan, where Jesus, at the request of his mother turned water into wine, which is in itself an allegory concerning the alchemy of love, gives us the metaphor 'turning water into wine', signifying an amazing accomplishment or deed, and there is no deed more amazing than the transformation of the soul, which is not only the main theme of the allegory but also the central theme of the Bible. Indeed, in ancient times the employment of metaphor and allegory was common in many religious systems.

For example, in ancient Egypt the Lotus was used as a metaphor of spiritual accomplishment; its life-cycle serving as an allegory of the way of spiritual attainment. Buried in the sediment at the bottom of the Nile, or perhaps a lake, the Lotus seed was understood to correspond with the soul and its existence in the physical body. At some point the soul like the Lotus seed must quicken or germinate and begins its ascent towards the surface and the presence of the sun. The first obstacle that presents itself to the

The Rose Priory Dialogues

Lotus seed is the sediment that presses down upon it, much as the affairs of the body and the world press down upon the soul restricting its progress. In breaking through the sediment the new Lotus shoot must traverse the waters above it, being careful not only to draw nourishment from the world through its roots, but also to draw nourishment from the sunlight filtering through the waters above.

In much the same way the soul, overcoming the obstacles of the mundane world must traverse the psychic world. Water has long been used as a metaphor for the psychic world, which at the lowest level is full of negative and destructive thought-forms and associated feelings. Metaphorically, these may be seen to correspond with the sediment that concentrates at the bottom of large bodies of water such as a river or lake. Here the metaphor becomes extremely interesting, because the water at the bottom of a river or lake is full of sediment, making it far murkier than at the surface, much like the lower, more bestial aspects of our life in this world. It is something we must rise above if we are to experience the clearer waters of consciousness that lie above the dross of our imagination. In this allegory, it is implicit that the growing Lotus, which is synonymous with the aspiring soul, rises slowly through the waters of the psychic world, avoiding being waylaid by the phantasmagoria therein, and keeping its attention focussed on the light. Inevitably then, as it ascends it becomes increasingly aware of the presence of the light and warmth of the sun, which is synonymous with the presence of the Divine. Eventually, sustained more and more by the Divine Light the soul breaks through the waters of the psychic world into the spiritual world represented by the clear light of the sun, where it spreads its leaves, as it were, and begins to flower. It is a beautiful allegory, and I have done little justice to it with this brief description. You should reflect upon it; it has much to tell you. Also, you should take note that spiritual allegories and metaphors are rarely static, dealing as they do with the rhythms of life that constitute the life-song of the soul.

Another, more complex example is the Graces or Charities, the constant companions or children of Venus Aphrodite, the goddess of Beauty. Opinions differ about whether they were her companions or her children, but they are generally portrayed as being three sisters dancing with their hands interlocked, and were a favourite subject for many artists, particularly during the Renaissance. They represent a synergy of movement that rests on the spiritual and cosmic dynamics of Emanation, Fixation and Return, more commonly described in terms of Procession, Rapture and Return. As the companions of Venus they denote the circle of Divine Love manifesting in the sphere of human life through Beauty, which corresponds with Procession, Love with Rapture and Joy with Return. This cycle of giving, receiving and returning expresses an underlying cosmic imperative that is observable in the laws of thermodynamics, but is more poetically expressed in the astrological principles of Cardinal, Fixed and Mutable signs."

"What?" said a quiet voice from the back of the room, "I'm sorry to seem so dumb but would you please explain what you mean by that last statement, especially that bit about the cycle of giving, receiving and returning expressing an underlying cosmic imperative; and how does that relate to the Laws of Thermodynamics or Astrology?" "Patrick, it's good to see you again, how's the leg?" "healing very well thanks, the plaster's off and I'm walking with the aid of a stick." Patrick waved his walking stick in the air to show it off. "but seriously, brother Marcus, I didn't really understand what you were saying a moment ago; please explain?" "I'm glad you asked," replied Marcus with a smile on his face. "Thermodynamics is concerned with the study and science of energy. We receive our energy from the sun which in the form of light enters our atmosphere and is transformed through photosynthesis into many different life-forms. It then returns to its source via the complex path of evolution. The same principle can also be said to apply to 'life' which emerges from God and evolves through many different forms on its return to its source. In astrological terms all things consist of one or more of four elements; Earth, Water, Air and Fire, and each element follows the same cosmic process of emanation, fixation and return. This is clearly demonstrated in the concept of Cardinal, Fixed and Mutable. The Cardinal Sign is the primary emanation of an element; the Fixed sign is the consolidated expression of the elemental archetype; and the Mutable sign demonstrates the process of entropy in the disassembling of the form and the return of the energy to its source. Does that make sense, Patrick?" "Some of it does, but I guess I'll have to think about the rest, thanks."

"That's inevitable, Patrick, it's a profound subject requiring a great deal of thought. However, consider the following, it might help you to understand. In the sphere of the soul, Beauty is the manifestation of the Divine, it acts as a beacon or light to which the soul is drawn; Love enraptures the soul with the object of its desire, and Return brings the soul back to the Divine in a state of

Metaphors & Meditation

Joy via the object of its love. However, before such an elevated state can be achieved the soul must evolve beyond the carnal drives of the instinctive nature and develop the innate but undeveloped faculties of discrimination and compassion. An interesting description of that development may be found in Plato's Symposium, where Socrates discusses the evolution of love. It is well worth reading, and you should not be put off by the different ideas he covers. It is not so much the detail involved as the concept of the evolution of human ideals from the carnal to the spiritual that is important.

Recognising metaphors and allegories is quite easy once you get your eye in, but understanding them requires time and commitment; they were generally devised as objects of meditation with many levels of appreciation. Consider the following allegory from the New Testament. It is the story of the nativity of Jesus Christ. The Gospels inform us that the angel Gabriel was sent by God to a young virgin called Mary, to whom he announced that she was to conceive by the Holy Spirit a child who would be called the Son of God. The Gospels also inform us that her child, Jesus Christ, is "the true light which lighteth the life of every man that cometh into the world," that this light was born not of the flesh or of the will of man, but of the will of God; thus firmly indicating that the true nature of Jesus Christ is beyond the rationale of the human intellect. The Gospels add that John the Baptist is the forerunner of the Lord, that he baptised people and taught them Repentance as the precursor to spiritual regeneration.

The allegory is suggesting that before we can become aware of the spiritual reality that is the basis of our existence we must change our ways, ways conditioned by nature and dictated by habit. To do so requires that we first recognise that this life is not the apex of our evolution, or the end goal of our existence. It then follows that we must give up being a reactive creature subject to our carnal nature and take upon ourselves a new way of life, a life of spiritual discipline signified by the washing away of sin in the baptism of water. This new life of spiritual discipline will eventually emancipate the soul from the bondage and influence of matter, and in doing so it will become a pure or virginal soul. In this allegory the purified soul is symbolised by the Virgin Mary, implying that before the Christ-Child can be born, that is to say, before we can become aware of the presence of Christ, the soul must be in a state of purity, that is to say, virginal. In the language of the mysteries, when the sphere of sensation is free of all forms and movements, then it is possible to become aware of the spiritual reality that is 'the true light which lighteth the life...'

The use of such stories to convey spiritual truths was commonplace in ancient times. For the majority, who could neither read nor write, a story or visual image was a very useful and practical means of recollection, and therefore perfect for meditation. How many of us today realise that before the turn of the twentieth century a great many of the population were unable to read and write and that before the eighteenth century few people in Europe were literate. However, during the eighteenth century Europe went through a revolutionary growth in commerce and industry. We call it the Industrial revolution, but it was also a social revolution and one of its major effects was to stimulate an equally revolutionary development in the field of education as the need for a literate and numerate population grew. Previously, literacy was the privilege of the nobility, the clergy, the professions and some merchants. The majority of the population had little need or call for literacy as communities were generally small and everyone knew everyone else. Generally, information was passed, and agreements were made, by word of mouth, although in some instances arrangements and contracts were written down. These apart, people generally communicated by the spoken word and a their word was their bond. Indeed at the turn of the twentieth century many of the population still remained unlettered.

Spiritual teachings were also given verbally and more often than not were given in the form of a story; indeed, the Bible is a collection of such stories, stories that many accept as true historical accounts. However, these stories also conceal great spiritual truths that were thought too profound for the uninitiated; consequently many subtleties were employed in maintaining and safeguarding them. They were designed in such a way that they could be discussed and interpreted on different levels; each level giving a deeper insight to the story, which for the sake of this discussion might be understood as having four modes of interpretation: Literal, Allegorical, Moral, and Mystical. This method of interpretation applies specifically to the life of the soul on its path of spiritual regeneration, not to political or historical secrets and intrigues; and when the scriptures were first written down in the sixth century BC, an event necessitated by the Jewish exile in Babylon, the same principles were employed in their construction.

The Rose Priory Dialogues

Such methods have been in continual use for countless generations. Philo Judaeus, who lived in the Egyptian city of Alexandria in the first century AD, wrote extensively about the allegorical interpretation of scripture. Much later, Moses de Leon, who lived during the late thirteenth century, likened the scriptures to a nut, a nut with a shell of literal meaning on the outside and an essence or mystical meaning within. He taught that the word Pardes, which means Garden or 'paradise', is a cipher concealing an esoteric understanding of existence. Each consonant of the word PaRDeS denoting one of four levels of interpretation and meaning; thus: P stands for the literal meaning; R stands for the allegorical meaning, particularly in the moral sense; D stands for the metaphorical meaning, particularly in the symbolic sense, and S stands for the mystical meaning. Arthur Edward Waite, an English mystic, whose writings spanned the late nineteenth and early twentieth centuries, describing the same thing, said that P equals the literal, R the symbolic, D the allegorical, and finally S signifies the mystical sense.

However, the literal interpretation of Scripture should not be set aside as we seek the deeper teachings; for the literal interpretation contains a code for living a wholesome life, a life that forms the platform for the more subtle work of the spirit. Sadly, many people waste their time seeking codes and ciphers that might reveal material treasures and knowledge of great secrets, and doubtless many more will lead themselves up the same garden path in search of the same." Marcus hesitated, then added; "Yet, there are ciphers and there are treasures, treasures far greater than fame or fortune, but they are all directed towards self-knowledge and the path of spiritual regeneration."

Marcus stopped talking; he could see people thinking about his words, and that soon enough one would speak out. Sure enough, a moment later a woman in her mid-thirties leaned forward and spoke; "Hi, my name is Paula; what I would like to know is this, are you saying that all religious texts are composed in the manner you described – as allegories?" "I can't speak for all," replied Marcus, "but many of the scriptures of the world's religions that I have examined have been, most certainly." "Even Hindu texts such as the Upanishads?" queried Paula. "Oh yes, especially the Bhagavad-Gita. It is said that it embodies at least seven levels of interpretation, and the Upanishads, although they present a beautiful spiritual teaching that is in many ways unveiled, have buried within them profound mystical teachings that are not so obvious. Sometimes they are presented in allegorical form and sometimes as metaphors; the Katha Upanishad is a wonderful example." Paula thought for a moment, then said; "What is the use of such allegories; why not just write what you mean, plain and simple? It seems to me that a rational explanation and common-sense guidance is all we really need." "There are some things," replied Marcus, "that the rational mind just cannot deal with. It is after all a creature of duality designed to deal with the space-time environment. The experience of the spiritual reality, which is the subject matter of our meetings, lies beyond the rational mind because it is of the nature of Unity. We can think about it, we can talk about it, but our rational mind cannot comprehend it, it just does not have the tools. Spiritual allegories are useful devices the soul may use in meditation to transcend the limitations born of the rational mind, and understand through inference and non-rational experience something of the spiritual reality. This has long been known in the schools. " "What do you mean by inference and non-rational experience?" said Paula in a puzzled voice. "What I mean is that we may experience spiritual reality in the form of an all encompassing love, in the form of a 'peace that surpasses all understanding', or in the form of a presence that cannot be articulated, or, occasionally, in the form of an inspiration that slowly percolates into our everyday experience. By such experiences we may know with a certainty that defies explanation, or we may infer from our experience something of the transcendent nature of the Divine. In either case the experience generally leaves no room for doubt. That's what I mean." "Thank you for that," Paula replied, "I don't wish to seem difficult, but I come from a background where the literal interpretation is the only interpretation. I shall give some thought to your words."

Marcus sat back in his chair, a few went to the bathroom, and I secured another coffee from the table. One man, I didn't get his name, said to Marcus; "You continually refer to the subject of meditation, I thought it was an eastern discipline, not western, yet you refer to it as if it was important if not central to the spiritual life of the western world. Is there really any truth in that? If there is its news to me." "It depends what is meant by meditation," replied Marcus. "In traditional terms meditation is a discipline that enables us to withdraw from the world of the senses into the interior realm of the soul, which according to most if not all spiritual teachings is the starting point of spiritual regeneration. Meditation requires the development of two basic skills; to be still and to concentrate the mind. To be still simply means being able to relax very deeply for an extended period of time, it's not so difficult. On the other hand, to concentrate the mind is a much harder task, although not as difficult as you might think. It merely requires a desire to engage with the interior world that is greater than the desire to engage with the world of the senses. Unfortunately, it is an imperative that cannot be avoided. However, if the desire to engage with the interior world is sufficiently strong then the skills of concentration come readily enough. It is essentially an introspective process, although it is often undertaken in group settings.

Today many people have an interest in Meditation, but traditionally it was never a discipline undertaken on its own, outside of the parameters of a spiritual curriculum. Indeed, in Christian terms, although meditation plays a central role, the path of spiritual perfection involves a systematic programme of spiritual endeavour that begins with an unquenchable desire for divine knowledge. It is a desire that is gradually realised through the application of specific ascetic disciplines, such as the purification of the instinctive nature through the education of the senses, appetites and desires – a time consuming work. Another important discipline is the control of the tongue, learning not to speak unless absolutely necessary and developing the ability to enquire and listen without interruption – a tricky undertaking closely allied to another, the examination of conscience, which is perhaps, the beginning of meditation in earnest. However, the main discipline is meditation on the scriptures and the maxims of faith embedded therein. This begins as a process of internal reasoning based upon a given passage of scripture, leading eventually to a higher state of consciousness, where the soul becomes aware of the presence of the divine. Dwelling in the presence of the divine is, in fine, the art of contemplation, a state which cannot really be described except, perhaps, through prayer or through parables – which are, as we discussed earlier, spiritual allegories.

These disciplines are very ancient; indeed, they were ancient in apostolic times. No soul has ever transcended the limitations of this world without engaging in the modification of consciousness that is implicit in these and other such disciplines. Indeed, true contemplation rests upon them in the same way as the lotus rests upon water. Furthermore, the higher mysteries of the Sanctuary are meaningless without them. It is probably true to say that from the earliest times the discipline of meditation has been central to most, if not all of the religions of the world. No single religion or religious system has had a monopoly of that discipline, although in recent times some have acquired the reputation for being the supreme exponents of the art. However, every culture has had need to develop its own system of spiritual perfection in which meditation plays a central role, and it would be extremely naive to assume that any one culture has precedence over the others.

Bearing that in mind, we can honour the Rishis of ancient India, who long ago withdrew from the common life into the deeps of the forests to engage in spiritual disciplines and further their spiritual aspirations, in which meditation was central. The same is true of the prophets of ancient Israel who in the wilderness of the deserts lived a strict life of Asceticism, as did the desert fathers of the second and third centuries, who congregated in the deserts of the Levant, and inspired the western world with the monastic ideal, in which meditation was of critical importance. Indeed one of the central methods of meditation handed down from the desert fathers, known to monastics simply as 'the ladder' or 'the way' is still in use today. It is formally known as *Lectio Divina*, or 'Divine Reading' and consists of the slow repetitive reading of a passage of scripture until it is known by heart, followed by meditating on its significance.

Traditionally, the reading, or Lectio, is read aloud repeatedly until the passage is known 'off by heart' with the emphasis on the act of listening. If the sacred text is read by another, those listening areexpected to repeat the words with their lips, under their breath as it were. This listening is no mere act of hearing; rather it is an act of attending with the whole of one's mind, engaging as much of one's being in the reading as possible, thereby cultivating the ability to perceive something of the soul of the text. The act of attending or listening is called Meditatio or meditation, which involved a reasoned engagement with the text and its significance. In times gone by the response to the meditatio varied, but often taking the form of spontaneous extemporary prayer, chanting or singing hymns etc. This response is known as Oratio. At other times Oratio took the form of inspired writings that in some way related to the Lectio and Meditatio. Those who persevered with this discipline found that the Oratio subsided into a quiet state of rest in what has been described as the 'Presence' of

The Rose Priory Dialogues

God and was traditionally called 'Contemplatio' or contemplation. Abiding in that 'Presence' is the basis of true contemplation and the experience of that Presence is the bedrock of unshakeable faith.

Lectio Divina is one of the oldest methods of prayer used in the Church. It is also embodied in the works of Philo of Alexandria and is clearly expressed in the work of the Pseudo-Dionysius particularly in his book *On the Divine Names*. It was enshrined in the Rule of St. Benedict and became one of the distinctive features of monastic life. This is not the case today; indeed, the most popular methods of meditation to be found in the modern world are themselves products of the imagination of that world. They are essentially guided phantasies that derive more from a syncretic blend of Spiritualism, Yoga, Buddhism and Shamanism than from any traditional school of pure meditation, oriental or otherwise. Many of these methods can be traced back to the ideas and practices employed by esoteric schools of the last hundred and fifty years, but there have been significant contributions from the various psychodynamic processes that emerged, particularly in America, from the 1950's onward. These processes, although deeply influenced by the materialism of analytical psychology and behaviourism, and invariably defined in the psychological language of Freud and Jung, are to be found at the heart of many modern systems of self-development."

As Brother Marcus spoke it occurred to me that I was listening to someone who had spent his entire life engaged in studying his subject. For the first time I understood that he was indeed a monk, not just an old man in a cassock, but a dedicated man in the service of the Church. What I found particularly interesting was his knowledge of the scriptures and teachings of other religions. He seemed to address them all as if they were of equal value to his Christian scriptures, which I must say was quite impressive. I wondered where he found the time to study them all; indeed, this was turning out to be quite an interesting evening. As I was musing about this I lost track of his words, for how long I'm not sure, but my attention was brought back to the discussion by Louise, Leo's girlfriend, saying, ".... but I must say that I find meditation really frustrating. Every time I try to meditate I end up feeling quite agitated and my body aches, in fact I often end up feeling worse than before I started. I much prefer activities such as singing or dancing, or even reading, perhaps meditation just isn't for everyone."

Marcus looked at Louise; his gaze seemed far away, as if he was looking into another world. "Your words, or words very much like them I've heard from many people; interestingly some of them have since become great exponents of meditation. I think the truth is simply that the ability to meditate takes time to learn. At first some, like you, find that when they engage with meditation they either become physically very uncomfortable or their minds become more active than usual, bringing the endeavour to a frustrating halt, others find that they cannot escape from their responsibilities in the world; their concerns seem to dominate their thoughts. Well, in my experience the main problem is that we begin with expectations far beyond our understanding; naively assuming we can just meditate proficiently from the beginning, but the truth is that mostly we don't have the slightest idea what meditation is about. It is not an objective in itself but a means of obtaining an objective. It is a discipline for the spiritual edification of the soul, and anyone who is serious about spiritual development needs to develop some proficiency in that discipline, which comes only with persistence and patience – there is no easy road or short-cut.

Earlier I told you that effective meditation requires the acquisition of two basic skills; learning to be still and concentration. Without them no one will ever be able to engage in meditation with any degree of skill. However, although it takes a little time it's not really that difficult, learning to be still is simply learning to relax. The deeper you can relax the better, fortunately any degree of relaxation is a good starting point. It is also important to bear in mind that in learning relaxation you do only that, without trying to think, or without trying to meditate. It is a fact that neither relaxation nor concentration is meditation; they are simply tools used to enhance or facilitate meditation, and you can develop them without unnecessarily vexing yourself speculating about whether or not you are achieving meditation.

There are many different methods of relaxation available today; most can easily be utilised by the student and do not usually take long to develop. The method I was taught is a simple technique of teaching the body the difference between tension and relative relaxation. It is easier than it sounds. I was simply asked to clench my fist and then let it relax. When I had done this a few times I was encouraged to do the same with every muscle and tendon I could. I started with my toes, then my legs, then my finger and hands, then my arms and so on. After a while I was shown how to do this in co-ordination with my breathing, before long I could relax anywhere, and often did. But as I say, there are many different methods, almost any one of them should do.

"Concentration, on the other hand requires that you be interested. As I said earlier, your interest in the interior world has to be greater than your interest in the things of the world of the senses. It was a point my teacher made to me on many occasions, his words were "your love of the Spirit must be greater than your love of the world – you cannot serve two masters". It is a fact as true now as it ever was. If the love of the Spirit is established within you, then concentration is far easier than if it is not. It is the same for any discipline; anyone studying a science is expected to be able to concentrate on their subject – to think deeply about all of the factors involved – and it is no different with the spiritual life. Therefore, if your love of the Spirit is truly greater than your love of the world then developing a little understanding of the chemistry of consciousness will greatly facilitate your ability to concentrate, although I am not so sure this is the time or the place to engage with this subject; it is quite complex."

Marcus then fell silent, members of the group looked at each other uncertain about what was going to happen next, had he finished, or not? One man, in his fifties I think, spoke out. It was Nick, he had been a fireman for most of his working life before an accident had ended his career and he had been pensioned off. In conversing with him I had discovered that he, like Leo and myself, had a life-long interest in the esoteric. "Marcus, I've travelled the best part of a hundred and twenty miles to be here, but, I'm not sure if I'll be able to get here next week, so I would be extremely grateful if you were to tell us something about what you mean by the chemistry of consciousness." Several others joined in, myself included, entreating Marcus to continue. Marcus relented and said he would, but qualified it by saying that as there was so little time available he could only really touch upon the subject.

"Although we are spiritual beings," he began, "we are subject to the forces that rule this world. By this I do not necessarily mean spiritual forces, although they obviously play their part. In this instance what I'm talking about are the natural forces that in obedience to divine law govern this world; and that includes our bodies. You might not like hearing this but at least ninety-five percent, if not more, of our physical, emotional and mental experience is defined by the chemistry of our body and the environment we live in; biology determines almost everything we do, and if we don't recognise or accept this fact then we will struggle to make any progress in this work. Most of us believe that we have the freedom to do whatever we choose, but that is a fallacy; just about everything we do in this world is conditioned and influenced by our environment. Yes, we do make choices, but they are conditioned choices. We are conditioned from the very beginning of our lives by our families, by our environment, by local and international politics, by climate, by social etiquette, by our need to secure a career and raise a family, to establish our place in the community, and so on. This conditioning is continually reinforced moment by moment, nanosecond by nanosecond. Only when we are able to accept this fact will we be in a position to begin the work of spiritual regeneration and emancipation." I could tell by the look on everybody's faces that they weren't expecting to hear this, in truth neither was I, but it made a lot of sense. Instead of an irreconcilable polarisation between atheism and religion, here was a point of view that accepted both positions and implied a dynamic that had a direction that was both meaningful and spiritually transcendent. I'm not sure how many of the others realised what he was saying, but they were definitely giving him their full attention.

Marcus continued, "Given this situation, where much of who and what we are is determined by our environment, especially our personal environment, by which I mean the body, it is imperative that we should know a little bit about it, how it influences our thoughts and feelings – how it impacts on the chemistry of our consciousness, so the least we can do is explore some of the principles involved, don't you agree?

One important area of human experience that affects us very significantly is tension and stress. Most of us see Stress in terms of intolerable social conditions, which may well be the case some of the time, but there is far more to it than social dynamics. All matter exists in a natural and fluid state of tension established upon the electromagnetic forces of attraction and repulsion. When states of tension change, the effects can be very destructive. Climatic variations illustrate this very clearly, for example, consider the impact of a heat wave, a sudden freeze, a drought or a tornado; any one of these can be very destructive. Indeed many people die under such conditions, as do many creatures. Like all life-forms we function at our optimum within a very narrow band of tension, beyond the parameters of which we enter into conditions of Stress.

Obviously there are also events in our daily lives that increase tension and produce stress, and some are more stressful than others, for instance, the death of someone we love, a divorce or separation, moving home, work insecurity, money or health problems, domestic strife and child care issues. I'm sure the list is almost endless, but they all have one thing in common, they are instrumental in generating stress and that is an important consideration for any student undertaking this work, because the mechanism of stress that affects us at these obvious levels is the same mechanism that affects us at less noticeable levels, and if we are going to be effective in meditation then we should try to understand it, at least to some degree. Now, I am going to try and describe this mechanism as best I can, but if any of you struggle with it, don't worry, we can discuss it at length on another occasion.

Our ability to survive in this world is based upon our ability to respond to real or imagined threats. Usually our response to threatening situations is either to fight or run away. This response is generally known as the Fight/Flight Mechanism; it is our instinctive reaction to danger. This mechanism is governed by the hypothalamus, which is a control gland in the centre of our brain. It is the primary link between two systems, the endocrinal glandular system and the autonomic nervous system. It directs the "fight or flight" response to danger via the autonomic nervous system.

The Autonomic Nervous System consists of two parts, the Sympathetic and Parasympathetic nervous systems. The Sympathetic Nervous System is the mechanism that enables us to respond and adapt to stimulation – be that pain or pleasure. It controls the upper limits of physical activity, generating a state of arousal that initiates movement concerned with survival. Some of its functions include stopping digestion, opening the airways of the lungs and increasing heart rate and blood pressure, in effect preparing our bodies for action. The counterbalance to this is the Parasympathetic Nervous System, which controls the lower limits of physical activity and is responsible for maintaining and conserving the body's resources. It regulates body maintenance, cell growth, digestion, relaxation and sleep. Some of its functions include the slowing of respiration and the decrease of heart rate and blood pressure – preparing our bodies for inaction, as it were.

The trigger for the F/Flight mechanism is the presence of certain hormones in our system, some of which stimulate the Sympathetic Nervous System to arouse the body; and before anyone asks, hormones are chemicals that transfer information between cells, controlling the function of various organs, and regulating metabolism. Unlike information sent via the nervous system, which is transmitted very quickly and has an immediate and short-term effect, the effects of hormones are felt over a longer period of time. Most hormones are produced by the Endocrinal Glandular System. This system is controlled by the Hypothalamus which emits chemicals that either stimulate or suppress the activity of the pituitary gland, which is thought to be the 'master' gland of the endocrines. This has a cascading effect throughout the Endocrinal System.

The term anxiety describes a subjective experience that is often expressed emotionally, such as in tears or aggressive and reactive outbursts etc., but rarely articulated beyond a vague generalisation. On the other hand, the term 'worry' describes the same experience but it is often related to a specific issue, the difference being merely a question of focus, in either case the chemistry is the same, an increase in the activity of the Sympathetic Nervous System. Thus, rumours of imminent redundancies at work may be interpreted as a threat to our security and well-being, indeed the very thought of the implications will ramp up the activity of the Sympathetic Nervous System, and when there is no closure, as the case may be with such rumours, the Sympathetic Nervous System will never really switch off, resulting in a prolonged build up of tension and stress.

For those engaged in this work, anxiety may be viewed as a barometer of the activity of the F/F mechanism, rather than simply being treated as an emotional state, although it is invariably something we perceive by feeling. The point I must emphasise here is that how we feel influences our thoughts, and what we think influences our feelings, consequently, if our thoughts are negatively charged, such as the redundancy example suggests, then anticipating problems will stimulate the F/F mechanism and increase our anxiety levels, which will reinforce our negative interpretation of the problem; thereby establishing a destructive cycle. Recognising this cyclic process is the first step in being able to understand it, and if we can understand it then we can modify it, either by taking the negative charge out of it, or giving it a positive charge through a change in our thinking.

Today the gym has all but replaced the Church; it has become the new temple in which we devote much of our recreational time to exercise, sport and athletics, in effect using the Sympathetic Nervous System for recreation. It is therefore only natural that we approach meditation with the same mindset.

Metaphors & Meditation

However, as many have discovered, when attempting meditation, instead of the anticipated peace and calm, they soon find themselves physically uncomfortable and their minds more active than ever. Most give up in frustration and do something else. Yet there is no mystery to this; they are simply in a Sympathetic Nervous System mode, as most of us are most of the time, because that is the nature of the modern corporate world – it never stops.

One of the most notable features of the Sympathetic Nervous System, and of anxiety in general, is rapid and or shallow breathing. In contrast, one of the main characteristics of the Parasympathetic Nervous System is a slow deep breathing. Now contemplatives have known since time immemorial that by regulating the breath, by slowing it down and deepening it, a state of calm serenity can easily be established in the place of anxiety and agitation. In effect through the use of the breath we can switch from the Sympathetic Nervous System mode to the Parasympathetic Nervous System mode, and in understanding a little about its chemistry we can establish a stable biological and psychological platform to engage in meditation. The key is simply managing one's breathing, learning to slow it down and to deepen it, and, combining it with the imagination to develop a method of relaxation. In short, breath control is the key factor in controlling the Autonomic Nervous System and the Endocrines; and it has been central to successful meditation for millennia. Concentration follows as long has you have something to concentrate upon, but let me remind you, meditation is not the objective, it is merely a tool." With that said Marcus stopped speaking and leaned back in his chair, smiling quietly to himself.

The Rose Priory Dialogues

Everyone present had something to say, the questions came thick and fast, but eventually the general consensus was reached that the subject should be addressed another day, when there was more time, and when everyone had thought about it. However, Marcus did emphasise that an academic qualification in biology was completely unnecessary for the understanding of this subject. "What is required is an attentive mind, and a willingness to enter the interior kingdom of your own soul in a state of wonder and quiet humility, that is all that you need to start." The discussion ended with a closing prayer. Some people left almost immediately, a few, myself included, lingered drinking coffee and talking. Leo introduced me to Marcus, who had heard a little about me from Leo. He knew I'd been in India and asked me questions about my travels and my opinions about what I had seen. He seemed genuinely interested, especially about the mystical side of India. He slipped out of the room for a few minutes and came back with a little book. It was an English translation of the Bhagavad-Gita. He gave it to me, recommending that I read it, and if I so desired, to come back and discuss it with him. I was very touched by this and gave him my word that I would read it and return; little was I to know what a profound influence it was to have upon my life.

I was also curious why a Christian monk should give me a Hindu religious text to read. I thought that he might have suggested a Christian text, but he never even mentioned one, all he talked about was the beauty and wisdom of the 'Gita', as he called it. He informed me that although it might be based upon an historical event, it was in fact an allegorical tale about the soul's path of evolution from the common state of human ignorance to its destined state of spiritual enlightenment; and that every soul must take this difficult path, that there was no easy way or royal road, merely a path of internal struggle, the beginnings of which are described in chapter one. He suggested that I think of Arjuna, the main subject in the story, as a representation of myself, and Krishna as the manifestation of the knowable aspect of God. That the battle was an internal conflict within the soul of Arjuna, who had to decide between his familiar world of the senses and all that such implied, and the spiritual reality that beckoned – the kingdom of heaven if you will. The main text consists of a dialogue that takes place between Krishna and Arjuna in the middle of the battlefield between the two armies. On that battlefield Krishna teaches Arjuna the Way of Spiritual Enlightenment. I had read the Bhagavad-Gita before, but I had never before heard it described in this manner. He made sound quite exciting, and I looked forward to reading it again with new eyes.

Part Three

A Chemistry of Consciousness

The Bhagavad-Gita is not a long story and I must have read it three or four times before the next meeting. The beauty of it lay in the fact that it was written in plain English; indeed the translator must have worked really hard to make it accessible to simple minds such as mine. With the guidelines set by Marcus I was able to see another side to this ancient tale, a side that spoke of an intangible something that lay at the heart of the human soul, yet could not be accessed by my inquiring mind. It lay just beyond my reach, as if it were the other side of a curtain, a curtain made of the finest mind stuff, yet as inpenetrable as a Black Hole. I found myself being led into moments of deep reflection about the purpose of my life, and even though I had only been reading it for a few days I found myself tentatively exploring my mind, looking for the elusive Atman. It eventually dawned on me that meditation was indeed a tool, and that I was unwittingly engaging with it, and as I did so I realised that the objective was truly self-knowledge. However, it also became apparent that the mind is a very big and scary place, and that some kind of map would be extremely useful. I knew I had to talk to the old monk about this, and I was sure he knew that as well.

The Rose Priory Dialogues

One afternoon, Leo and I met in the tea-room at work. He had just picked up a load of furniture from the auction rooms and I had just returned from a delivery. We had not really seen each other since the meeting, except in passing, so it was the first opportunity we had to talk. We exchanged pleasantries, made a cup of tea and sat down at the 'genuine formica' table that stood in the corner. I asked Leo if he had read the Bhagavad-Gita. His response was interesting, he said, "Oh yes, I've read it many times, in fact I'm still reading it. Marcus gave me a copy some months ago and I can't put it down. Have you read it yet?" "Have I read it? I've been reading it non-stop for days; I must have read it three times at least. But tell me, why is it that a Christian monk should be so fond of promoting Hindu religious texts? I think that's really odd." Leo laughed, "I know what you mean, I thought the same, so I asked him why he did that. His response was that in today's secular world it was a great introduction to the mystical philosophy and therefore a good introduction to the Bible, which he thought was far too complex for beginners. At some point he will probably encourage you to read the Upanishads as well – they're absolutely wonderful." I asked him how long he had being attending these meetings, and what had first sparked his interested in mystical things. He said; "When I was about ten years old I began to have odd experiences around certain buildings and places, sometimes even near certain trees and rock formations. Consequently, I've spent years studying and exploring Ley-lines and energy fields, that sort of thing. The Rose Priory is located on an intersection of two major Ley-lines. One cuts across from east to west, the other seems to run southwest to northeast. I met Marcus some months ago when I was dowsing near the rectory. Since then I have been attending meetings every week. I have never come across anything like them, or anyone like Marcus."

"What do you think of him," I said, "Well, I don't really know what to say," replied Leo, "As far as I can tell, he is what he appears to be, a monk devoted to the mystical life, about which he obviously seems to know a great deal. He has taught me a lot without charging me or imposing any obligations, but I get the sense that I've only seen a tiny portion of him; a bit like the tip of the old iceberg sort of thing. I have never seen or heard him engage people in politics or religion beyond the natural concerns of conscience, and he doesn't push people to join the order he belongs to, in truth he doesn't push people to do anything. He's a bit of a mystery really." I asked Leo if he knew anything about the order, Leo said that Marcus had informed him that it was a contemplative religious order devoted to prayer and meditation. "He doesn't really talk a lot about it, he's not really reluctant or secretive, he just doesn't see the point in satisfying the curiosity of non-members; however, I once saw the order curriculum lying on a table in the library, and it seemed pretty demanding to me. If Marcus has worked his way through that, which he probably has, I can see where his breadth of knowledge comes from. You should ask him, see what he says, I don't think you'll offend him." I made a mental note to see if I could get Marcus to one side and have a chat about these things. After all, I had spent the last few years wandering around half the planet looking for genuine mystics, and here I find what looks like a genuine mystic living in the backwoods of the west country, and what is even more surprising he's a bloody Christian. It's a non-negotiable situation for me; I have got to know more, even if it is only to eliminate another illusion.

The Rose Priory Dialogues

We arranged to rendevous at the Atlantis café, as we did the previous week, and then we parted, each to or own chores. I to make another delivery and Leo to unload his van.

As arranged, I picked up Leo and Louise from the Atlantis café, it was drizzling rain, a fine clinging rain, and the air was heavy with the smell of wood smoke and damp earth, it felt really autumnal. We arrived at the Priory quite early and made our way to the library, passing two black-robed members of the Order on the way. They barely noticed us as they passed us by conversing softly. I was sure that one of the figures was a woman, I thought for a moment that I should ask Brother Marcus about that, but then remembered that he had said that the Order drew its members from both sexes. There were quite a few early birds, which annoyed me somewhat as I was hoping to catch Marcus alone, however, it didn't matter as he wasn't there, but the fire looked inviting, even more than last week, and that cheered me up immediately. We all found a seat around the fire. About twenty people turned up that evening, although not so many were smoking. I noticed this time that the average age of those gathered had to be somewhere between thirty and sixty, I hadn't noticed that before, and the balance between men and women was about even. I don't know why but that observation puzzled me. Marcus turned up a few minutes later, poured himself a coffee and sat down in the same old chair as last week. As time went by I came to realise the old cane chair was 'his' seat, and nobody else ever sat in it.

Just as before, the meeting began precisely at eight o'clock. Again, as the clock began chiming the hour everyone stood up and gradually fell silent. Marcus began the meeting with a prayer, a prayer so evocative and full of grace and wonder that I almost became tearful. Marcus looked around him and spotted one or two new people and made the same preliminary announcement as he did last week. As the weeks passed I noticed that when he recognised everyone, he never made the preliminary remarks, I guess he didn't need to, although he always began with words that suggested there was no agenda, such as "What shall we talk about today?"

This evening was no different, Marcus asked for suggestions and several people requested that he continue with the subject of meditation, which they felt was left unfinished from last week. One person, a rather slim man, about thirty years old, addressed Marcus; "My name is Carl, I'm really interested in what you said about mediation last week, although I must admit that I left thinking that meditation was no more than a system of applied reasoning; surely there must be more to it than that. I mean, where is the spirituality in thinking?" Marcus sat still for a moment, he seemed to look within himself, to gather his thoughts, he sat for a moment, completely oblivious of his surroundings, then opened his eyes and spoke; "Carl, I don't know if you remember, but last week I described a meditative system called Lectio Divina, although many of its exponents simply call it 'the ladder' or 'the way'. This method begins with collecting the mind in one place by focussing the attention on one thing, and in Lectio Divina the focal point is a verse or line of scripture. Now when meditation is simply an application of concentrated thought upon a given subject we call it reasoning and as such it is a discipline well worth cultivating. But when it is used as a tool within a spiritual discipline then it becomes something else, it becomes a rung on a ladder of spiritual ascent.

The spiritual discipline I am referring to is also known as Asceticism, which is a term derived from a Greek word for 'exercise' or 'training' that describes an austere system of physical and mental discipline aimed at combatting vice and developing virtue. It was a discipline that was well established in the Greco-Roman world. At its higher levels this form of asceticism used psycho-spiritual processes to separate the soul from the body and its negative influence. Christian mystics on the other hand, following their own traditions developed Asceticism along another line altogether. Rather than seeking purification through separation, they sought purification through unification – the unification of the body, soul and spirit in Christ. For the Christian mystic the spiritual work, or *ascesis*, was a means of engaging the whole person in the spiritual life, central to which were the practices of prayer and meditation. The method of prayer employed was generally known as 'ceaseless prayer', it is a method based upon a directive of St Paul, who advocated all to "Pray without ceasing". In the desert communities of the Levant, during the third and fourth centuries, many forms of ceaseless prayer were developed that invariably consisted of short formulae never longer than a phrase or two. The value of this kind of prayer is that it may be used habitually, becoming a self perpetuating reflex that sublimates the incessant mental noise that is our common experience of the mundane world, and in its own context prepares the mind for communion with the divine."

A woman called Deirdre spoke out. I had noticed her the previous week, her thick gypsy-like black hair cascading onto her shoulders in loose curls was unforgettable; "Excuse me, Marcus, but that last statement, 'a self perpetuating reflex that sublimates the incessant mental noise,' I don't really understand it, what does it mean?" "Oh" said Marcus, "What I meant is simply that through the habitual or continuous use of a short phrase, in this case a short prayer, it is possible to keep the attention completely occupied, and all extraneous thoughts which normally form the background noise of our minds, are either absorbed into the overall tone of the prayer or dispersed by its presence. The context or meaning implicit in the prayer forms the subject matter of meditation and establishes the soul in a relationship more appropriate for communing with the Divine. That is what I was trying to say. Do you see that now?" "Yes," replied Deirdre, "I think so; it's a bit like a mantra isn't it?" "To a point," replied Marcus, "but the objectives don't always converge, one important difference between them is that in ceaseless prayer you should understand the words, and, you should always engage with the meaning of them rather than the sound of them." "Thanks, I think I've got that; just one more thing; how does the context of the subject matter establish a relationship more appropriate for communing with the Divine?"

Marcus considered the question. After a moment or two he said, "Think of the soul as being a tree with its roots deep in the diversified earth of coarse sensation, its trunk rising through the spheres of human experience and its canopy high in the sublime atmosphere of the presence of the Divine. With that metaphor in mind where would you place your sense of self right now, in the roots, perhaps, or somewhere on the trunk, that is to say, somewhere on the field of human experience in the mundane world? The truth is our awareness oscillates up and down the trunk of the tree. Sometimes we are lost in a sea of pure sensation and occasionally our awareness is high up the trunk in the realm of pure thought, but most of the time our awareness is engaged with the things of the senses and the demands of the mundane world. However, in the method of prayer we are discussing, the context of a prayer, that is to say its meaning, its significance, draws the soul upwards, beyond the things of the mundane world towards the canopy, as it were. The important point to understand is that to regain that which we have lost we must rise above the mundane world, and prayer and meditation, as used in Lectio Divina, are tried and tested methods of achieving just that. Do you understand now, Deirdre?" "Yes, thanks. The model of the soul as a tree is really interesting, is there any material written about it?" "It is not a subject to be read about, but experienced," replied Marcus, "on that basis everything you need you already have, you simply need to reflect upon it, to see it within yourself." "Oh!" She replied, and fell silent.

"The notion of ceaseless prayer," Marcus continued, "may appear incomprehensible to many, particularly to those who look upon prayer as a form of plea-bargaining with God, but for the desert fathers and their successors, prayer meant and continues to mean something else entirely. It is the secret language of the soul, a language synthesizing thought, image and emotion into one thing in a manner that transcends the limitations of our mundane existence. This kind of prayer requires that our entire conscious mind should be focussed upon the ultimate object and purpose of life, which is God. It is then the most profound expression of our love, by which we are able to join 'in one spirit' with God, and it is in this context that meditation is employed as an aid for gathering and directing the faculties of the soul. At first the work is laborious, because initially the mind is like a puppy new to the leash, it continually seeks to break free, but eventually it learns to 'come to heel' and even finds satisfaction from it. Thus, in Lectio Divina the initial work consists of concentrating on the words of the text chosen from scripture, but it is only the beginning of the

A Chemistry of Consciousness

journey; at some point you will discover that engaging in prayer on the same terms is equally efficacious, indeed, prayer and meditation ultimately becomes one thing.

As to the question 'where is the spirituality in thinking?' I would ask you to be mindful of who it is that thinks, for I was taught that which thinks is a living spirit made in the image of God. It should be obvious, even to a casual observer that this image isn't simply a physical representation, but a symbol or metaphor alluding to the divine potential residing at the heart of our being. It is the ideal that we are driven by necessity to express, and the evolutionary imperative 'to be' or 'to become' is the mechanism by which the unfolding of that divine potential will reach its fullest expression. In short, within every human being there is a spiritual being seeking to realise its true 'divine' nature. You may not realise it but thinking is a divine act, unfortunately; for most of us our thoughts are far from the divine, indeed, they are actuated in the chemistry of the natural world, which stimulates thought at an instinctive level. The articulation of which is the language of the mundane world.

I was informed that if I would commune with the Divine then I must rise above the carnal influences of the mundane world, and that can only be achieved by daily purifying mind and soul that they may reflect clearly the light of divine inspiration, and to that end I was taught a metaphysical language to better articulate that inspiration. It is not greatly appreciated by the novice, never mind armchair mystics, just how much of the spiritual work consists of emancipating the soul from the shackles of that world. Therefore, please understand, no one just 'does spirituality', we must become it, but first we must grow out of the mundane world, and that in itself is a most serious undertaking, then we are able to grow in the spiritual life. The first requires courage, effort and willpower; the second requires humility and patience, and evolving our thinking is a part of both, because we don't stop thinking when we realise our spiritual potential."

Marcus stopped speaking and looked around him, as if he was waiting for someone to speak or do something. No one did, so I took the opportunity to ask him a question, "Last week you lent me a copy of the Bhagavad-Gita, and I must say that I have not been able to put it down since. You seem to be saying that the Hindu Atman described in the Bhagavad-Gita is the same as the image of God described in the Bible; what I'm trying to ask is this, is the soul, which is made in the image of God, the same as the Atman?" "The short answer to that is yes, and the long answer would fill volumes with qualifications and explanations," replied Marcus, "however, it should be said that the objective in both the Bible and the Gita is the same – the spiritual regeneration of the soul – but the approach differs. In the Bhagavad-Gita the god Krishna is described as the, 'Atman that dwells in the heart of every mortal creature', but the majority of people know nothing of its presence, and throughout their lives the majority of people, so it is written in the Gita, 'pass by the place of my dwelling, here in the human form, and of my majesty they know nothing at all, who am the Lord of their soul.' The Gita describes the Atman as a creature of light covered by the darkness of self-delusion, the substance of which is described as rage, lust and avarice. In other words the spiritual reality of the Atman is hidden from the soul by the chemistry of the mundane world, and the physical body is part of that world.

In the language of the Bible, Creation may be understood as the creation of the human soul, an immortal being whose only vesture is a garment of pure spirit, or perhaps of light. In this state the soul exists within the 'Presence' of God, in what we call Paradise, where all of its needs are fulfilled by that divine Presence. Therein time and space have no place as all beings share in the unity and omniscience of God. The Fall, a subject of continual debate in some circles, describes a descent from that divine presence into the material world of duality, where clothed in a 'coat of skin', the soul experiences birth and death, pain and suffering, the needs of the flesh, and the need to work to survive; but perhaps worst of all the soul experiences separation from the Presence of God, and consequently, the darkness of complete ignorance – a spiritual amnesia not so different to the state of the soul as described in the Gita. In this fallen state the soul knows nothing and has nothing, other than the experience of the mundane world, hence the wandering of the people of Israel, as described in Exodus, signifies the soul's growing evolution as it engages with the mundane world through what it perceives via the senses, and to which it is driven by the incessant demands of the animal nature of the body. In both the Bible and the Gita the essential message is that we must overcome the influences of the mundane world if we are to win the kingdom of our soul and gain access to the spiritual reality concealed therein.

Given the nature of some of our physical experiences it is not surprising that many people make the mistake of hating the body as if it were evil, but the body is not in itself evil; more often than not it is the consequences of our ignorance and our selfish actions that generates evil – the body is merely the field of our experience, and until we realise that fact we will forever be at the mercy of its creaturely needs and appetites. It is therefore important to understand the nature of the body, to educate it, and to sublimate its nature in the spiritual life, thereby transcending the negative influences of the mundane world, or in the words of the Bhagavad Gita, drawing the sword of discrimination and 'slashing delusion to pieces.'

What Marcus said made a lot of sense to me, but something else he had said a moment or two earlier kept echoing around my mind, and I had to ask him about it. "You said a moment ago that you were taught a metaphysical language to better articulate inspiration; would you explain that; I mean what is a metaphysical language?" Marcus smiled, rather he grinned. "I'm not sure I can answer your question fully, but I will say this much, our everyday language is the articulation of thought actuated in the natural or mundane world. It is a domestic and civil language. We understand it and its nuances to a greater or lesser degree, and with it we are able to get along with our neighbours. It is not a language that is generally useful to explain complex mathematics or chemistry or even philosophy; each of which have their own specialised language. The same may be said to some degree of the legal profession, or indeed, any of the professions. A metaphysical language is, then, a specialised language that enables the soul to engage with spiritual concepts and realities more effectively. It is made up of symbols and signs that follow certain rules and conventions which have little to do with the domestic world and its environs. As with any language, to become adept in using it requires a great deal of practice. However, applying it to the mundane world, without the appropriate experience and understanding, is completely meaningless; indeed, mumbo-jumbo would describe it quite nicely."

I thought to myself 'at least he answered the question, however, I don't think I really understood him', but it did bring

A Chemistry of Consciousness

back to the fore the subject of the chemistry of consciousness, which we were going to discuss this evening. I asked him about that. He said, "The last time we met we discussed the concept of Tension and Stress in relationship to meditation. The model that we used is a useful device that allowed us to look at the influence of biology upon our thoughts and feelings without having to take a degree in the subject. It also introduces us to our selves in such a way that we can take an objective look at how we are physically and emotionally conditioned and moved by events taking place in the world, and more importantly, how we might adapt in positive and constructive ways to some of the challenges we may have to face. Building on this platform I would like to introduce another principle concerning the chemistry of consciousness.

When we close our eyes and focus upon what is taking place in our minds, we can break down what we perceive into three components; feelings, images and thoughts. Indeed our entire awareness and appreciation of the interior world is based upon the volatile chemistry of these three components, and it is with the understanding of this chemistry that so much of the work is concerned. The truth is that when we look at these three components what we actually perceive is the threefold structure of one thing, a thought-form. Every thought-form consists of an image, a feeling and an idea or intellection.

For convenience let us call an idea or intellection a thought; as such we may consider rain as water falling from the sky, and we might further muse about the climatic cycle that gives us rain – that would be thinking, or we may imagine what rain looks like, for example recalling from our memories images of a light spring shower or a downpour; alternatively, we may bring to mind feelings associated with our experience of such examples. It is axiomatic that every thought form consists of all three components, but one of them will usually predominate. For example, the word dentist will make some people shudder, indeed, when some people think of dentistry they are filled with fearful emotions, evoking memories of sitting in a dentist's chair and everything associated with it, including the memory of pain and discomfort. On the other hand the smell of a cigar might remind another of Christmas, evoking pleasant memories of childhood. In both of these examples the feeling predominates. In other situations it is the image that is uppermost. This is particularly so with objects of desire, be it the desire for another person, for professional status, or for something like a dream house or car, moreover, it also applies to objects of aversion such as a menial task or job that we think is beneath us. Every experience we have ever had generates thought-forms, and every experience we will ever have will be associated with thought-forms, some will be new and unique, but by far the majority will be based upon past experiences, and therefore upon established thought-forms, or memories. Indeed, memories consist of thought-forms and groups of thought-forms of varying complexities.

Last week, I described how the majority of our experience, including what we think, is conditioned by our biology. I should add that this is so because the body is designed, programmed if you will, to survive in this world. I was taught that this biological programming is an expression of a primal urge or instinct 'to be', which manifests itself in the form of two secondary instincts, 'reproduction' and 'survival'. This is true not only for humanity but for all creatures, because without exception all life-forms are driven by them. They are so powerful that the majority of us will go through our entire life devoted to fulfilling them and nothing else, and rarely, if ever, perceiving the spiritual basis and background to them. Almost all of us unconsciously build our identity in the context of these biological drivers; in fact they determine our thinking, particularly in the way we establish our lives around the complex relationships we form with the rest of humanity. We aspire to a place and a status in the community that gives us sufficient personal respect, and the resources to attract a mate and provide for a family. In our corporate world this means a career that will fund a mortgage and give us sufficient money to keep a family and afford a life-style. This requires an appropriate education, not only in academic studies but also in relationship skills; all of which are set in the context of a community of people by and large striving for the same things. For most of us our family and career constitutes our life. In human terms this is the mundane world. Thus, we identify the most personal and intimate part of our selves with the instinctive nature and appetites of the body, and we invariably fail to recognise that our thinking is a product of biological drives interacting with our social environment.

Our ability to think is inherent, it is a function of the soul, as is the mechanism of thought, thus, the rational, visual and emotional faculties are faculties of the soul; but what we actually think is conditioned by both the animal nature of the body and by our environment. How we overcome this conditioning is through self-knowledge; we begin with learning something about ourselves, because without self-knowledge there is only ignorance. There is nothing new about this, our ancestors understood it, perhaps more than we do today. On the entrance to the temple of Delphi in ancient Greece was engraved the legend 'Know Thyself', and it is with this in mind that I have introduced you all to a simple method of self-exploration; a method that is safe, accessible and applies to the spiritual life." A man's voice from the back called out, it was Nick, I think; "Your description of the triad of thought, feeling and image is very interesting, but what am I, or indeed anyone else supposed to do with this knowledge, how are we supposed to use it in our spiritual aspirations?" "Well," said Marcus, "you might explore your own nature, it would help you more than you can imagine right now." "How would I do that, I mean in what context, where would I start, and how would it relate to meditation?" replied Nick. Marcus looked at his watch, the evening was getting late and he had hoped to cover more material. "Everything depends upon intention; meditation is by definition undertaken with a specific purpose in mind, but, that purpose, particularly at the beginning, can ever so easily be undermined by our biology, which has its own agenda. However, we will only understand our biology and the way it influences our thinking through observation, thus self-observation is the first step on the path of self-knowledge. We generally see our thoughts, imaginings and feelings as separate independent functions, and fail to see them as aspects of one thing functioning as a complex chemistry of consciousness that is driven by biological needs and which invariably defines our personality, and until we do so we will remain, as it were, spellbound by that chemistry knowing nothing of the real self dwelling therein.

Discovering the nature of the real self is a slow process that has often been likened to peeling away layers of an onion, and one of the layers is the ever-present veil of thought forms that hangs before our mind's eye. In themselves they are nothing more than the product of the chemistry of consciousness, they are not consciousness itself. As I pointed out earlier, these thought forms consist of thoughts, feelings and images. What is noticeable to the

A Chemistry of Consciousness

contemplative is that because such forms are rooted in biological conditions that profoundly affect the motivation and will of the thinker; they make us all slaves to our own biological needs and appetites. It is therefore necessary that if we are to arrive at a true understanding of how things are, we must learn to distinguish between the thinker and the thought form, between the chemist and the chemistry, and with that objective in mind I have provided you with tools to assist you to do just that, but how you use them is dependent upon you and you alone."

At this point Marcus suggested that we take a break or call it a day. The general consensus was for a short break and then to resume the meeting, assuming Marcus was ok with that. Several people, including Leo and Louise made such a good case that Marcus agreed to continue, but first made sure everyone had some idea of what he was talking about, that they were clear about the influences that biology had upon our psychology and therefore upon our ability to meditate. Several people had questions about the implications of his ideas concerning thought forms, but decided they could wait. I was really interested in understanding what lay beyond the 'veil' as Marcus described it. I asked him about that as soon as we resumed the meeting. Everyone else seemed happy with the idea so Marcus agreed to talk a little about it.

"The emancipation of the soul depends upon it first being able to make the distinction between the real and the unreal, between the Self and not Self, concerning which there are two main approaches, I have shown you one in the path of meditation, it is a means by which it is possible to pass through the veil of thought-forms that separates the soul from the inner reality of its own being. The other is the path of devotion whereby the soul gives itself over entirely to the Divine through prayer and the sacred rites, in which the life of the soul is sublimated in the service of God. In Hindu terms this path is called Bhakti, the path of devotion; the other is Jnana the path of self-knowledge through meditation. In either case discrimination between self and not-self is the first stage in the work of attaining the regeneration of the soul, and consists of learning to distinguish self from the physical and psychic nature. It is a process that begins with the desire to withdraw from the world. Some find this extremely difficult, yet, in truth, the real difficulty lies not in withdrawing from the world but in establishing a stable presence in the interior world. There is no mystery to this, it is simply a question of motivation; which calls for more than good intentions and an effort of will, indeed, success will come only to those whose love of the Divine is stronger than their love of the world.

Generally speaking, it seems to be the case that of those who take up the spiritual life most are led to it through suffering. It might be through personal illness or the death of a loved one, through war, famine or disease, or perhaps through the loss of something important and or meaningful, indeed, it might well be a combination of such things." A man of some fifty years or more, a little overweight, and with a mane of white hair tied in a pony-tail, interrupted Marcus saying, "Excuse me, Marcus, I'm terribly sorry to interrupt you, but you seem to be suggesting that suffering, be it through sickness, famine or war, is a part of the natural order of things, part of God's plan, as it were. I find that difficult to accept. Is it really what you are suggesting?" "No, Ivor" replied Marcus, looking at the benign smile of the chubby grey-haired man. Ivor, I later discovered, had spent many years travelling the world and had been a part of the British Scientific

A Chemistry of Consciousness

Survey team in the Antarctic. All in all he was a very capable man. "It is not what I am suggesting. What I am saying is that over the course of history it has been observed, that as a rule many of those who undertake the spiritual work have suffered in one way or another. Of course there are those who in their pain deny God and the spiritual reality, maintaining that if there was a God then there would be no suffering, or that they want no part of a god who makes creatures suffer. Alternatively, there are people who have an intuitive sense of a divine providence guiding all things; in this they trust yet take no part in the religious life of their community. However, the people I am alluding to are those who recognize that beyond the fleeting, albeit painful experiences of this transient world lies a reality that transcends duality and all that such implies, such as ignorance, suffering, old-age and death. The Bhagavad-Gita states that: 'Men take refuge in me, to escape from their fear of old age and death....knowing me they understand the nature of the relative world and the individual man, and of God who presides over all action.' Whatever our personal philosophy, it is obvious that our life on this earth is relatively short. We are born, we mature, we age and then we die. We may prolong our life indefinitely, but that we must die is inevitable, and no one dies of good health. That some react negatively to these conditions is inevitable, but some are driven to understand that supreme reality in which everything finds its existence and it is to such as these that I refer. Does this make sense to you now, Ivor?" "Yes, very interesting, thank you."

Marcus continued, "Whether we believe in one life or many lives it rests in our own hands whether or not we continue to be reactive creatures ever responding to the stimuli of the world, or seek knowledge of the permanent reality underlying this transient existence. One might suppose that if the conditions in this world were always fine then there would be no motivation to evolve or to move on, however, there are those who recognise that the problems we face in this world provide the impetus for us to evolve, both physically and spiritually; science drives the exploration of the material world whilst religion forms the basis of our understanding of the spiritual world. In material terms death may well be the end of physical existence, but in spiritual terms this world is not the end goal of our existence and thus we must continue our journey, be it from incarnation to incarnation or be it a spiritual journey to the stars. Thus it is said of this world: 'the birds have their nests, the fox has its lair, but the Son of man has nowhere to lay down his head.' Consequently, whatever it is that acts as a catalyst, somewhere and at some point we become sufficiently motivated to engage with the spiritual life with the sole purpose of following the advice given by those who have gone before, i.e.: Know Thyself, which is to seek and obtain direct knowledge of the spiritual reality existing within the depth of our being.

Self-knowledge, then, is the knowledge of the permanent spiritual reality that forms the basis of our existence. That reality is the 'Light which lighteth the life of every man that cometh into the world'. However, for many the idea of a spiritual reality is little more than a vague sense of 'otherness' that is often suppressed or denied. Yet, despite such commonplace negativity there exists a body of knowledge that speaks of the spiritual reality in a most beautiful and evocative manner. It speaks of a reality that lies beyond the realm of the senses; at the heart of which dwells an immortal life essence, a divine archetype that anyone may come to know directly. From the earliest times knowledge of this reality has been handed down from generation to generation, the same teaching expressed in different ways by different cultures, that each wave of incarnating souls might have access to the knowledge of their true nature. Thus the New Testament teaches that the Kingdom of Heaven lies 'within' and that knowledge of it should be sought before anything else; similarly, the Bhagavad-Gita commends us to 'turn within'.

The process of 'turning within' is a discipline which our more enlightened ancestors practised and taught along with prayer as being the only sure means of attaining direct knowledge and experience of the Divine Nature that dwells within us all. This discipline begins with learning the art of meditation. However, the majority of people who engage with meditation do so as a pleasant form of deep relaxation, as an antidote to the stresses and strains of the modern world, and so should we all. But, we should also be mindful of the fact that relaxation is an essential component of meditation as a spiritual discipline, without which it would be impossible to enter the quiet state that is the first stage in the art of meditation. The means by which a state of relaxation is established vary; some schools advocate the practice of Yoga or the use of elements of it. Some prefer the use of breathing exercises or chanting a mantra and some recommend bio-dynamics; it matters little whichever one uses so long as a controlled physical stillness is established. The exception to this is the use of drugs, which is not advisable as their use does not constitute 'control', quite the opposite in fact, because the effect of drugs cannot be reversed or stopped at will; they open doors that cannot be readily or easily closed; which is an important consideration as there is more to meditation than relaxation. Indeed, the deeper waters of meditation may be disturbing at times as unexpected changes do occur within the psyche, significantly affecting our biology with impressive and sometimes negative psychological results; and if we do not understand the part biology plays in our life then progress in this work will be undermined as we continually react to the biological changes that occur in our lives." At this point Marcus stopped talking. Someone, Ruth I think, passed him a glass of water. We sat in silence, each engaged with their own thoughts about what they had heard this evening. The time was late, well after midnight and the only sounds audible were the clock ticking in the corner and the occasional crackle from the fire.

I'm not sure what time I left the Priory, I remember sitting in silence for a long time, or so it seemed, but then time at the Priory didn't operate on normal terms. Sometimes a few minutes took hours to pass and on other occasions hours passed in minutes. I do remember sitting in my room with a cup of coffee watching the sun rise reflecting upon Marcus's words. He seemed to return again and again to a singular theme – that nothing exists in this world that is not subject to change, that these changes are determined by our biology, that there exists in all things a constant factor that is formless and not affected by the changes taking place in the world, that it was possible to discover this constant in a state of meditation, and through which it was possible to transcend the delusory world of the senses and discriminate between that which is real and that which is unreal. I had asked him just before we left if this was correct and I had understood him correctly. He thought I had a reasonable grasp of the situation. He added that when we begin the process of withdrawing from the world of the senses we enter a realm of constantly shifting images, emotions and thoughts, wherein it is difficult to establish any true bearing. In such a confusing environment it is much easier to recognize the transient, which is the unreal, than to recognize the real. The Pseudo Dionysius, perhaps the most influential mystic of the western world, understood this simple yet profound truth. His teachings emerged in the late fifth or perhaps the early sixth century, no one knows precisely when although they were discussed at a council in Constantinople in early sixth century.

Marcus then went to a bookcase and took out a book, It was, he said, a translation of *On The Divine Names* by the Pseudo-Dionysius. He opened the book and read from it: "Just as the senses can neither grasp nor perceive the things of the mind, just as representation and shape cannot take in the simple and the shapeless, just as corporeal form cannot lay hold of the intangible and incorporeal, by the same standard of truth beings are surpassed by the infinity beyond being, intelligibles by that oneness which is beyond intelligence". He closed the book and quietly said; "The images and emotions that dance before the mind's eye are but pictures and sensations which come and go like the wind, some are terrible to behold and some are beautiful, but it must be remembered that they cannot truly do any harm except by identifying with them, in believing them to be self, then we can inflict suffering upon ourselves. As discussed earlier, images have a direct relationship with emotions; one influences the other, by recognising this fact we may be free of their influence. By observing how images give rise to associated emotions and thereby altering the chemistry of the body, and by observing how emotions give rise to associated images, thereby altering the chemistry of perception, we learn the importance of relaxation and non-attachment. No longer are such experiences blindly accepted as 'me' or 'mine'". I was beginning to see what he meant by the veil, and left the Priory lost in thought about the inner reality.

Part Four

A Tradition Revealed

Over the next few days I could do little but think about the last few words read from *On The Divine Names*. They encapsulated everything Marcus had been speaking about, and perhaps that was his intention, to show me that the subject matter we were addressing was as ancient as time itself. If it had been his objective then I was grateful; indeed, I had every hope of finding a copy of *On The Divine Names* for myself. Thus it was on Saturday I found myself in the old district heading for the Atlantis café to set myself up with a cup of coffee and just possibly a piece of cake, before engaging in the pleasurable task that lay before me.

I parked the car in the multi-storey car park overlooking the centre and walked slowly down the hill towards the café. I passed several art galleries, their windows displaying the latest creations of well known artists, and was about to pass a newage shop full of essential oils, incense-sticks, tarot cards and all of the equipment necessary to furnish either a magician's temple or a witch's coven, when out of the shop stepped Ruth. I think she was as surprised to see me as I was to see her, and anticipating my next question she said; "Just buying some incense; how lovely to see you, where are you off to?" "Oh!" I said, "I'm on my way to the Atlantis café for a coffee, care to join me?" "What a splendid suggestion" she said, taking my arm, "lead on MacDuff." Arm in arm we set off along the pavement chatting about the Priory when a voice behind us said, "Is this a private party, or can anyone join in?" Leo's voice was recognizable anywhere; Ruth responded, "We're going to the café for coffee and cake, coming?" "I thought you'd never ask," he replied. "Where's Louise?" I asked. "She's at the bank, she'll join us as soon as she's finished; we're also heading for the café."

We entered the café, which was warm and full of the aroma of coffee and freshly baked pastries. We ordered and took a seat by the window, looking out onto a road busy with traffic. The café, being situated on the corner of a steep hill was blessed with a small forest of traffic lights. It was a combat zone where pedestrians and drivers did their best to wind each other up. Fortunately the hospital was only a a couple of hundred yards along the road so everyone was well catered for. Leo said; "I'm Leo and you're Ruth aren't you, we met at the Rose Priory, did we not?" "Yes, we did, and I'm pleased to meet you too" replied Ruth. I asked Ruth how she came to be at the meetings at the Priory. "I met Marcus through my mother. She was recommended to consult him by her GP; she had breast cancer, and things were looking very bleak for her. Whatever Marcus did, and neither are telling, her cancer went away. As a matter of fact her consultant told her she never had cancer in the first place. She introduced me to him for whatever reason a mother might have. She probably thought I needed curing of congenital irritability or something like that. I've been attending the Priory meetings ever since – they're quite extraordinary. But enough of me, what do you think?" "I'm not sure what to say" I

A Tradition Revealed

replied, "I've spent years looking for an Indian mystic and I seem to have found one that's a Christian instead – what can I say?"

Leo laughed and said; "Joe's a bit put out about that you know. Life is not matching his expectations. I think he hoped to settle in the sultry heat of southern India listening to the secrets of the ages being passed onto him by a great guru, instead he's met a Celtic monk who would probably prefer his students to be standing up to their knees in icy water, contemplating the weakness of the flesh and the nature of illusion." "Poor thing" Ruth said feigning sympathy. "I don't know about that" I said, "I have heard a lot of people talk spirituality during my travels around the world, but I've never heard anyone talk like this old monk before. Its not like he's selling anything, nor is he making life easy for us, it seems like he's just sharing his understanding, but if we are to achieve spiritual enlightenment, or regeneration as he call it, then we have to do the work, and that's fair enough isn't it? As a matter of fact I'm out today to see if I can find a copy of a book he suggested was worth reading." "What book's that," said Ruth and Leo simultaneously. "Its called *On The Divine Names*, and it was written some fifteen hundred years ago by someone called the Pseudo-Dionysius. Obviously it has been translated in recent times and I'm looking for a copy." "Have you been to the Wise Owl Bookshop yet?" queried Ruth, "I haven't been anywhere yet, I was just about to start when I met you two outside." "Well" said Leo, "If you don't mind, when Louise arrives we'll come with you, what do you think Ruth?" "Sounds good to me" she replied with a hint of glee in her voice anticipating

trawling through piles of long forgotten books covered in dust. "I
like looking for books."

As we were waiting for Louise, Ruth asked, "What did you
two think of last week's meeting at the Priory?" Generally, my
experience of Leo was that he is quite reserved, not big on letting
people know what he thinks. However, surprisingly, he responded
quickly to Ruth, saying; "I always leave the meetings with more
questions than answers, but the answers I do get are really
interesting. Marcus seems to put theory to one side, yet I can see
that he has a deep understanding of the theoretical side of the
subject matter; which is in many ways a blessed relief. I'm fed up
with those who know it all, spouting forth chapter and verse. It is
refreshing to meet someone who is prepared to deal with the bare
bones of the subject. Last week's meeting introduced me to a way
of engaging with the substance of my mind in a way that I can
work with; not necessarily with any great skill or understanding,
but hopefully, with practice that will come." "Its funny that you
should say that" I said, "I have been thinking since last week that
Marcus is simply introducing us to ourselves; enabling us to
engage with the very private and personal enterprise of
Self-knowledge. I know that when he introduced me to the
Bhagavad Gita he was introducing me to what I needed most. He
knew that, without a shadow of doubt he knew it, and I knew that
he knew it, and he knew that I knew he knew it. So when he
introduced me to the Pseudo-Dionysius, he was introducing me to
another part of the jigsaw; he didn't give me a copy, he didn't even
say I should read it, but he knew I needed to study it and so did I.
What I'm trying to say is that I believe there is a method to his

A Tradition Revealed

madness; he is operating according to a system and I'd like to know more about it."

Ruth seemed delighted with this response; "My thoughts entirely. You probably don't know this but the first time I met him he introduced me to the Chinese philosophy of the I Ching. He said that it would assist me in exploring my world. I have an enquiring mind, always asking questions, but how was he to know that? Anyway, as the Prior of a Contemplative Order I expect him to be operating according to a system, as yet I just have not had the opportunity to ask him what it is. In truth I've not had the nerve, I'm afraid that he might not want to answer me, so I haven't. Anyway, I'm thinking that perhaps between us we might find the ideal opportunity to question him about the system he, and probably the Order he belongs to. What do you guys say to that?" Well, we both thought the suggestion was reasonable enough and agreed that at the very next meeting we should look for the opportunity to interrogate Marcus about the system he uses and to be quite open about it.

Louise arrived, out of breath, having just climbed the many steps that ascended from the city centre. She looked pleasantly surprised to see Ruth and myself and asked Leo to get her a coffee. A tall slender woman with a bob of dark red hair, Louise commanded quite a presence, but she was not a forward or pushy type of person. A highly respected landscape architect employed by the city to protect the environment from pollution, she preferred, as I discovered over time, to be in the garden or walking the moors rather than the social amenities of the city. Furthermore, her skills in healing were well-known and many people preferred to consult her than go to see their local doctor. We sat talking for a while and then left in search of interesting books.

In the Wise Owl Bookshop, which is a bookshop specialising in esoteric books, I found a copy of On the Divine Names. The owner took us upstairs to his private stock, where the rooms were full of rare and interesting books about arcane subjects. Here he arranged his catalogues and met with his special clients. He appeared at first to be a contentious man who obviously didn't suffer fools gladly, but his knowledge of his specialisation was astounding. Moreover, as we got to know him over the course of time we saw beneath his testy exterior a really friendly and caring man.

The book was very short and I was able to read it and re-read it before the next meeting. I didn't see much of Leo at work, except for a brief moment to arrange picking him and Louise up at the café, as we were both out in our vans either delivering or collecting furniture. Come Friday I left work early enough to grab a sandwich and a cup of tea, although we were five minutes late for the meeting because of it. We offered our apologies and took a seat near the back. Carl, was asking Marcus how is it possible to tell a good teacher from a bad teacher, I caught his last few words which were, "If a person is interested in the spiritual life but knows nothing, how does such a person know if a teacher is good or bad, what signs should they look for?" Marcus replied, somewhat firmly, "People are drawn to this work through the awakening of their own soul, do you not recall, we discussed this last week? In real terms the teacher finds the student, or to put it more succinctly, the teacher and the pupil are brought together by divine providence. However, bear this in mind, no genuine teacher would ever ask a student for money in exchange for the teaching nor expect sexual favours, nor would any teacher allow a student to become emotionally dependent. These things apart, how would any student be able to judge the qualifications of a teacher? The answer is, they could not. At the beginning of a relationship the teacher will appear to be extremely knowledgeable; as the student progresses, the teacher will seem to be not so all-knowing. There will be a crisis-point where the student will challenge the qualifications and values of the teacher. This is a critical moment when the relationship is either consolidated or it breaks. A good teacher will allow what must be to happen. If the student consolidates the relationship then the teacher will begin to teach the student in earnest. At that point the teacher and the student become true brothers or colleagues in the great work of spiritual regeneration. Now, I'm sure you understood that, Carl, so do you have any more questions? No! Good! We'll get on then." If Carl had any other questions he wasn't given the opportunity to ask them - I think he had been firmly put in his place. Marcus then suggested that latecomers should not be late again as it was unfair to those already gathered. We latecomers grovelled appropriately, vowing never to be late again. "We shall see" replied Marcus.

I asked Marcus if the Order had women members. Given his shortness with Carl I thought I might be in for a roasting, but he answered me quite pleasantly. He said that the Order did have women members, and that as far as he knew it had done so from the earliest times. Before I could ask him how many, he said that the balance of the sexes fluctuated over the decades; currently he thought the balance was in favour of the Brothers rather than the Sisters. When I asked him how many Brothers and Sisters there were in the Order, he said he was unsure. He knew that there were twenty in this chapter, but he could only estimate the Order total being perhaps one hundred and twenty world-wide. Ruth, seeing an opportunity to learn more about the Order, said, "Marcus, I have been thinking for some weeks now that you seem to work according to some form of curriculum or system. Forgive me for asking but if you do then would you please tell us about it. Its not idle curiosity on my part, its just that there seems to be a consistency, a theme, as it were, and I wonder if you might share it with us?" Marcus didn't respond immediately, he just sat in a state of impenetrable silence. After what must have been an agonising couple of minutes for Ruth, he smiled to himself and spoke, "Every religion in the world functions within the parameters of some kind of system. I've studied a few of them, but there are far too many for any one person to study never mind understand. Within Christianity there are many systems employed, particularly in the religious and monastic orders. Indeed, the term Order implies a system or a rule that the members follow. For example, The Benedictine Order follows the Rule of their founder, St. Benedict, who lived in the first half of the sixth century. The Dominican order follows the Rule of St. Dominic, the Society of Jesus – the Jesuit Order – follows the Rule of Ignatius of Loyola. The Order of Dionysius and Paul has its own Rule, established by its founder, Mar Dionysius.

Members of any Order live according to their Rule and study the curriculum established or favoured by the Order. In the Order

A Tradition Revealed

of St. Denys, apart from studying the seven liberal arts and sciences, members are expected to study the Christian Faith, and furthermore, to spend some time studying the philosophies and mythologies of the religious systems of the world. One of the systems that we study is the esoteric theosophical system of Judaism that the world today calls Kabbalah. I shall try to describe it to you, but, you must understand that as a system it is not simply Jewish but the legacy of the ancient world transmitted through Judaism. It is a system that may be found within all of the cultures that succeeded the Greco-Roman world, which includes Christianity, but as we shall see, it's most well known form today derives from Judaism." Marcus paused and looked around, then said; "before I continue are there any questions so far?" No-one volunteered any questions so he continued.

"What I am about to give you is a background story about the evolution of a tradition of spiritual development that goes by the name of Kabbalah; it will take some time so prepare yourselves. Now it is generally accepted that the Kabbalah emerged in southern Europe during the closing years of the twelfth century, particularly in the region of Southern France and Eastern Spain. However, many professed Kabbalists believe that Kabbalah is far older than this; that it is the secret doctrine of spiritual development transmitted to the people of Israel through the prophet Moses more than three thousand years ago. Whatever the truth may be the impact of Kabbalah upon the deep waters of mysticism and magic has been both extensive and significant. Indeed, ever since the Kabbalah first emerged from the shadows of the sanctuary, in the late twelfth century, its teachings have not only influenced the mystical and spiritual life of Judaism, but have also contributed to the shape and spiritual direction of many of the western world's foremost esoteric movements – Rosicrucianism and Freemasonry among them – and have been central to such movements from the Renaissance to the present day." Someone behind me, I couldn't really see who, said in a somewhat frustrated tone of voice, "Hi, my name is Charles, this is my first visit. I hope you don't mind me asking but who is Moses and what is a prophet, I've heard the word before, but all I understand is that a prophet is some kind of fortune teller?"

Marcus thought or a moment, then said, "Charles, in biblical terms a prophet is a person who speaks through divine inspiration, declaring the will of God as it is revealed; prophets were very important in the life of ancient Israel. As for Moses, who was he? Well, for those of you who don't know, his life is described in Exodus, the second book of the Old Testament, where we are informed that he was born of Jewish parents and through curious circumstances was adopted by and brought up as a member of the Egyptian Royal Family. When he became an adult he was instructed in the ancient and secret wisdom of Egypt. Guided by divine providence, Moses emancipated the Jews from Egyptian oppression and led them out of the land of Egypt into the wilderness, where he formed them into a nation and led them to the 'Promised Land'. Whilst in the wilderness, Moses ascended the sacred mountain of Sinai, where he received a dispensation from God for the Jewish people. Following divine instruction he gathered seventy of the elders together and they were enthused with the Holy Spirit. Through this transmission they not only

A Tradition Revealed

received a spiritual insight into the meaning of the Law, the Torah, but also a spiritual understanding of the Soul of the Law. In this lies the source of the Jewish tradition we know as Kabbalah. Incidentally, this story may also be understood in allegorical terms. Does that answer you question, Charles?" "Yes, thanks, very interesting."

"My pleasure" replied Marcus, and continued, "At first the teachings embodied in the Torah were transmitted orally from generation to generation, that is, until the early part of the sixth century BC when Israel was invaded by the Babylonian army under the leadership of king Nebuchadnezzar. The Jewish Royal family and the ruling elite were taken into captivity along with many skilled artisans and craftsmen. Thus began the Babylonian Exile. During their captivity in Babylon, which lasted for about seventy years, the essence of the Mosaic teachings was committed to writing and gathered together in one work. This work is the written Torah and consists of the first five books of the Bible: Genesis, Exodus, Leviticus, Numbers and Deuteronomy.

After the death of Nebuchadnezzar, Babylon was absorbed into the expanding empire of the Persians. The Persian rule was a benign rule, and during the reign of their King, Cyrus, the Jews were allowed to return home, and rebuild their Temple. They also integrated the Synagogue, which had been instituted during their captivity as an alternative place of worship to the destroyed temple, with the reading and exposition of the Torah as its main objective. This was a very important development because it is the exposition of the esoteric interpretation of the Torah that forms the basis of the Tradition we call Kabbalah. And it was in the culture and spirit of the synagogue that it acquired its principal form and nature.

Although no longer in exile, Israel remained a subject state dependent upon a succession of contemporary super-powers, eventually becoming a province of the Roman Empire. In the year 66 AD, the Jews revolted against the Romans. In response, Rome dispatched an army to restore order and a bloody war ensued. Eventually, resistance in the country was eliminated and the Romans turned their full attention to Jerusalem. The Roman legions, led by Titus, began a systematic demolition of the city, culminating in the burning and destruction of the Temple – the focal point of Judaism. Making an example of the city, they slaughtered thousands of the inhabitants; those spared from death were taken as slaves or sent to the arena; the people who were able fled, seeking refuge in the many settlements of the Diaspora. From that time the Jews were 'a dispersed people'; a nation without a state and a religion without a temple. However, in the Diaspora Jewish refugees established a sense of community, and were able to preserve their identity in their religion. Yet, inevitably, the beliefs of the people of the Diaspora were influenced by the cultural environment they found themselves in, which was more often than not deeply imbued with Greek thought particularly that of Pythagoras, Plato and the Academy.

At this point Louise, who seemed quite animated, was forced, much against her nature, to speak out, "Marcus, before you go any further please tell me what is a Diaspora. I haven't a clue what the word means? "Oh" said Marcus, "did I not say, I'm very sorry; a Diaspora, or perhaps I should say the Diaspora, is the name for the

A Tradition Revealed

settlements or communities of Jews living outside of Israel. They first occurred as a result of the Babylonian destruction of the Temple in the sixth century BC, when large numbers of Jews settled in Babylonia and other countries bordering Palestine. They became a very important feature of Jewish life, particularly after the Roman destruction of Jerusalem in 70 AD, when many thousands of Jews fled from the Roman military machine that was bent on destroying them. That event is known as the Great Dispersion. Are you ok with that, Louise?" "Yes thanks" she replied.

"In the fourth century AD., the emperor Constantine transformed the world when he legitimised the long persecuted Christian Faith and gave it preferential status in the empire. He also played an active role in promoting Christianity and inaugurated an increasingly hostile policy towards paganism. As time passed, religions such as Judaism were either forced underground, to practise in secret, or to move to areas beyond the immediate influence of the administration. During the reign of Theodosius I, Christianity became the new state religion and all other forms of religious expression were restricted and penalised within the increasingly Christian Empire.

The spiritual teachings of the ancient world did not fade into obscurity, but were quietly integrated into Christianity through the influence of such men as Clement of Alexandria, Origen, St. Augustine, and the Pseudo-Dionysius. Indeed, the Christian Philosophers of the third and fourth centuries completely took over the Neoplatonic system, adapting it to suit the growing intellectual framework of the Church." Marcus stopped, and asked if everyone was keeping up. I was really glad that he did because I didn't have a clue what he was talking about. I heard the words but they meant nothing to me; so I asked him, "I'm sorry to interrupt, but that last bit about the spiritual teachings of the ancient world and Neoplatonism, what does any of that actually mean?" Marcus looked at me grinning, "Well you and your friends wanted to know about the system I am using, so I'm trying to explain it to you as simply as I can. Neoplatonism is the summation of Late Greek philosophy, a re-presentation of Plato and his successors' work and ideas expressed in the context of the teachings of Plotinus and his students, Porphyry and Iamblichus. It has strong mystical associations which have brought it into disrepute with many historians and theologians, nevertheless, its influence has been widespread and long-lasting, especially among the Jews of the Diaspora.

The most influential figure among the Neoplatonists was Plotinus, whose teaching proposes three principal modes or states of being to which he applies the term 'Hypostases'. The first he defines as The One, which is the prime source and principle of all being, the very ground of existence. The second as the Divine Nous or Mind, in which exist the archetypal ideas and prototypes of all Creation. The third, proceeding from the Divine Nous, is the World Soul, below which lies the realm of Nature, which constitutes the outer life of the World Soul, and last of all there is undifferentiated Matter – the last consequence of the outpouring of the One; it forms the lowest stage of the universe, and is thus understood to be the antithesis of the One."

A Tradition Revealed

"Where do human souls come from in this scheme of things, their source isn't obvious from your description, is it?" said Carl, Marcus looked at Carl and said firmly, "Patience Carl, patience, if you think about it you will realise that human souls proceed from the World Soul, and like the World Soul may also be subdivided into two or more parts, because a human being, Plotinus taught, is a microcosm wherein the principles of the Hypostases are reflected as Spirit, Soul and body. Below the sphere of the soul lies the material world, in which the soul's conjunction with matter and a material body takes place, and which Plotinus taught was a fall or descent from a higher state. It is from this fall or descent that the soul seeks redemption, and, to which Plotinus devotes much of his attention."

"Excuse me Marcus" said Leo, "this model seems to be very close to the Christian position; is this actually the case, I mean are they related?" "To a point" said Marcus, "Before the fourth century, before the Church was emancipated, much of the Christian teaching was considered sacred and not to be shared with outsiders, so it is difficult to know with any real certainty. However, much of the Late Greek philosophy did pass into Christian thought, so your observation may be accurate. However Plotinus' model of the cosmos is significant, in that he describes in literal terms what previously had been taught through metaphor and allegory and only experienced by the initiate during the celebration of the Mysteries. At the centre of this celebration, with all of its pomp, ceremony and drama, the consciousness of the initiate would have been elevated through the use of evocative prayer to experience the World Soul in the form of Demeter, and then after a different fashion, to experience the Divine Nous in the form of Dionysus. Plotinus believed that it was possible for individual souls, through the practice of contemplation, to ascend to the level of the Divine Nous, and there, in spiritual union, be absorbed back into the One. He describes the most important objective of the Mystery Schools as the direct experience of, and union with, divinity. The first part, which may be thought of as the 'Lesser Mysteries', was concerned with the separation of the soul from the carnal nature of the physical body. The second part, which may be described as the 'Greater Mysteries', was essentially concerned with the elevation of the soul beyond the reactive nature of the psychic world into the presence of divinity where union could take place. Much of Plotinus' thought can be seen in later Kabbalistic thinking, and also in Christian mysticism, so the connection is certainly there." Leo mumbled his thanks but seemed lost in thought. He often was at these meetings, so Marcus continued.

"In the centuries succeeding the great Dispersion the Jewish people consolidated their faith in the wisdom of the Rabbis, who were successors to the Pharisees, and in the Talmud, which became the cultural benchmark for all Jews. During the Second Century the oral teachings of the Jewish people were committed to writing They consisted of two parts; the first, the Halakah which embodied religious rites and ceremonies, civil and criminal law and jurisprudence in general; the second, the Haggadah, consisted of the thoughts, hopes, feelings and wishes of the Jewish people as expressed in the customs, myths, parables, proverbs and stories of the Torah. The arrangement of this immense amount of material

A Tradition Revealed

took two forms; the first, the Mishnah, is a compilation of Laws and regulations. The second, the Midrash, is a collection of commentaries on, and discussions about, the books of the Torah. The Mishnah and a collection of commentaries known as the Gemara together form the *Talmud* and, although not strictly a Law-Book it was eventually adopted as the only authority in matters of religious law. I labour this point to bring to your attention how important the Talmud and the commentaries that form the Midrash were to the Jewish people; and, how the use of such texts has been fundamental to the development of Kabbalism.

With the fall of the Roman Empire in the fifth century, civilisation rapidly declined and much of Western Europe entered a long period of ignorance, war, poverty and disease. The social structure of Roman civilisation was torn apart by invasion from without, and civil conflicts within. Education and the Arts fell by the wayside, to be maintained only by the Church. Whilst Western Europe lay in the grip of these 'Dark Ages', the Eastern part of the Roman Empire, centred around its capital, Byzantium, flourished. By the sixth century Byzantium had become the centre of civilisation in the declining Roman Empire, and was to remain an important centre of the civilised world until 1453 when it fell to the Turks. There were, nevertheless, some areas in Western Europe that were safe havens for the custodians of the 'Tradition'. One such region was the Moorish territory in Spain. From the middle of the 8th until the middle of the 11th Century the Moors ruled much of Spain from their capital Cordova, Their tolerant rule ensured a fruitful and luxuriant lifestyle for Muslim, Jew and Christian alike. Further north, Provence and the neighbouring region of

The Rose Priory Dialogues

Languedoc were also very tolerant of different cultures and philosophies, making Southern France an oasis of artistic and scientific excellence. The region supported not only the Cathars but also a large international community of Jews, Arabs, Greeks, Spaniards, Italians and Eastern Europeans, filling the intellectual environment with a dynamic mixture of Greco-Roman Neoplatonism, Dualism, and the esoteric teachings of Judaism, Christianity and Islam. Here the Grail legends and the poetry of the troubadours flowered, and the Kabbalah, as understood today was born. From the beginning of the thirteenth century Kabbalists began to emerge as a distinct mystical group, attaining considerable prominence in Southern France and Spain.

You must understand that when the Roman Empire collapsed Western and Eastern Europe went their separate ways, and only came together again in the centuries of the Crusades. It was because of the crusades that West European culture re-established its connections with the Eastern Empire and beyond. Arguably it was through this contact that a cultural renaissance took place that was to transform our world, and its epicentre was the city of Florence. Here, Marsilio Ficino, with the support of Cosimo de'Medici, became the founder and inspiration of the Platonic Academy of Florence, which was dedicated to the study and translation of the works of Plato and the Academy of Athens. Ficino not only translated into Latin the works of Plato but also the works of Plotinus, Porphyry, Iamblichus and Proclus, making many classics of the ancient world available to western readers. In doing so he and other members of the Academy created the conditions by which the study of esoteric Judaism could be safely

A Tradition Revealed

embraced in a sympathetic manner; and it was in this environment that the secret teachings of the Jewish mystics – the Kabbalah – entered upon the world-stage.

In the midst of this Renaissance a body of work was published called the Zohar, otherwise known as The Book of Splendours. It is the definitive work of Kabbalistic mysticism, and was composed in Spain during the late thirteenth century by Rabbi Moses de Leon, from where it circulated in manuscript form. In the latter part of the seventeenth century Knorr von Rosenroth a German Kabbalist translated important sections of the Zohar into Latin. His translation had a tremendous influence on western thought as it was the main source of information about the Zohar in European circles until the beginning of the twentieth century."

Marcus stopped talking and suggested a break. He stood up and left the room and people gathered into little groups, quietly chatting about the way the evening was developing. I heard a few people say in their own unique ways that they had never heard of Kabbalah before this evening, and one or two were sure it was the domain of black magicians and sorcerers. Leo and Ruth were listening to Louise when Marcus returned. He poured himself a coffee, looked around, asked if everyone was ready to resume, and sat down in his old cane chair. Everybody returned to their seats and Marcus began speaking, "Thus far we have briefly surveyed the historical background of the Kabbalah, but the question remains, what is it? As I said earlier, in the eyes of scholars it is an esoteric system that emerged within medieval Judaism. The word Kabbalah is closely related in meaning to what we understand in English by the word 'tradition' but not just any tradition, it signifies a body of knowledge concerning spiritual development passed on from generation to generation by oral transmission. One thing it is not is a study of esoteric literature. We can read all of the spiritual and magical texts that have ever been written and still end up knowing nothing about Kabbalah. Books, manuscripts, ancient scrolls and codices contain information, and information is simply data, it neither gives wisdom nor understanding; it is not knowledge. If Kabbalah is a study at all it is a study of the secret life of the soul in its relationship with God, the chemistry of which constitutes a secret doctrine.

To those who wish to explore Kabbalah as an intellectual exercise, wish them well, but know that in doing so they will not find the door that gives them access to its secrets. Indeed, there is no person or text on this earth that can give that knowledge; we must find it within ourselves, and finding the doorway that leads into that inner garden is no easy task. It does not require intelligence so much as awareness, nor does it require goodness so much as a willingness to be led by goodness. No one is so base that they cannot enter; yet they cannot take their baseness with them. However, it does require a dedicated heart and a persevering will." Marcus stopped for a moment. Looking directly at Leo Ruth and myself, he smiled, nodded and continued speaking – it felt like my mind had been read and he wanted me to know it.

"Thus far we have looked at the development of the tradition; it was a unique development in the evolution of the soul of humanity that flowed out of the ancient civilisations through the Greco-Roman world into our own. In truth if you were to seek, you would find the essence of Kabbalah in any of the world's great

A Tradition Revealed

religions, but the Kabbalah as we know it emerged in the context of our cultural evolution, and doubtless it will continue to unfold as our culture changes. The basics of Kabbalah are tools for the soul to engage in the exploration of its own spiritual nature – an inner life that unfolds in the context of the Bible; for the Bible is the heart of the Kabbalah. All Kabbalistic teachings concerning the inner life are set in a biblical context, and they are extremely subtle. Sadly, some people, even those who have never read the Bible, have strong prejudices against it. Many have heard stories from it as children and still think of it as children, while for others, perhaps the violence, contradictions, and challenges to our modern thought, make a formidable handicap. Yet, it is a handicap worth overcoming, for everything a Kabbalist might need is to be found in the Bible. However, we must first learn to read it as adults, as something other than a book of fables, and if you seriously want to engage with the Kabbalah you will probably need more than one version. The earliest written version is the Septuagint; this was the principal Bible used by both scholars and Kabbalists in the past. There are other versions – interlinear and parallel text Bibles; some of them are very useful, but be warned, the Bible does not give up its secrets easily."

"Excuse me, Marcus", interrupted Justin, who was new to the group, I'd spoken with him earlier in the evening; he'd travelled quite a way to attend. He informed me that he had heard Marcus speak at a lecture in London and felt drawn to find out more, hence his presence at the meeting. I later discovered that he was thirty-five years old but could easily have passed for twenty-five. He had been a professional photographer for most of his working life but had recently become a Bowen therapist; "I am finding the subject difficult to keep up with, isn't the Bible supposed to be written in code, with lots of secret and hidden messages about the future of humanity, and of the world?" "Yes" replied Marcus, "that's true, but the literal interpretation of Scripture is also valuable as it forms a platform for the more subtle work of the spirit. Sadly, rather than seeking the spiritual treasures hidden within it, people generally prefer to look for codes and ciphers that might reveal material treasures and knowledge of great secrets, and doubtless many more will continue to allow themselves to be led up the same garden path in pursuit of the same phantasies. Yet, there is more; there are ciphers, which are very difficult to crack, there are treasures far greater than fame or fortune, and there are secrets. The question is, how does one find them and how does one understand them? Well, the answer lies in where you direct your attention. A Kabbalist of the seventeenth century compared the Mosaic books to the body of a human being, the commentaries on them such as the Zohar, he likened to the soul, and the Kabbalah he compared to the spirit of the soul: ignorant people, he taught, may study the first, the learned may study the second, but the wise, he said, direct their contemplation to the third." "That sounds extremely elitist to me," snorted Justin, "I mean, surely if there are secrets locked in a code written into the Bible text, what's wrong with looking for them?" "That" replied Marcus "is for the individual to answer, as for myself I wonder what secret is greater than knowledge of your own soul, of knowledge of your source, your purpose here, and your ultimate destiny?" "I've made a real twit of myself, haven't I?" retorted Justin. Marcus laughed, "At least you're honest about it, however let's get on, shall we?" "Ok, I'll be quiet from now on," replied Justin with a sheepish grin on his boyish red face.

"One of the first tasks undertaken by a student is the development of a metaphysical language that enables the soul to function intelligently at a much higher level than our everyday language commonly allows. In Kabbalah this begins with learning the Hebrew alphabet along with all of the correspondences that go with it. It is not so much a foreign language that needs to be learned as a mystical algebraic system, a system that is capable of many levels of permutation and interpretation. Another task the student should undertake is to become acquainted with the cosmology on which the Kabbalah is based, as it will resolve many of the obscure issues that will arise along the way. Apart from anything else Kabbalah is a modelling system that enables the soul to put into perspective the matrix of human consciousness, and to understand the dynamics of that matrix. It is to this end that many Trees and maps are employed and directed." Justin couldn't help himself, the word were out of his mouth before he knew it had happened, "What trees and maps, where do they fit in, oops! Sorry", "No, don't apologise" laughed Marcus, "the question is a good one, and I'll do my best to answer your question.

The tree has been a key symbol in the life of humanity from the earliest times, and this is particularly true in Kabbalism. The reverence in which the tree is held is evident in every culture and civilisation that has kept records of its history. To the Ancient Egyptians the Tree of Life was a colossal tree that served as the central axis of the cosmos, on the summit of which perched the

The Rose Priory Dialogues

Phoenix, the symbol of immortality. The Sycamore tree was also used as a representation of the Tree of Life, from within which the goddess Nut dispensed the drink of immortality and the fruit which imparted the knowledge of Good & Evil, thus enabling the discriminating soul to reach the fields of Amentet, otherwise known as the underworld. In Scandinavian mythology, the ash tree Yggdrasil is the greatest of all trees; it is the world tree that holds together heaven, earth and the underworld. Nine worlds are believed to be contained within it. At its roots is to be found a fountain of sacred water that has the powers of purification and regeneration. It has three main roots, beneath the first is to be found the realm of the Frost giants, beneath the second the realm of man, and beneath the third the realm of Hell. One description speaks of a great cockerel, glittering like gold, standing upon its highest branch, another states that perched upon its highest branch is a great eagle, between whose eyes sits a hawk.

In Hinduism the tree is generally considered to be a symbol of universal life and immortality. However, to those living the mystical life it is a manifestation of the god Brahma, with the rest of the gods forming its branches. It is said to grow in Brahma's world in the midst of a lake called Ara, from which the waters of eternal youth are drawn. It has many names, but as the Soma Tree, the world-tree furnishes the divine ambrosia or essence of immortality. The Asvattha Tree, the sacred tree in Buddhism, imparts wisdom and produces the divine ambrosia – the food of immortality; and furthermore, provides a dwelling for the souls of the blessed. Under the Asvattha Tree the Buddha sat and went through different stages of consciousness, until he attained enlightenment and received the knowledge of the sources of mortal suffering. The world-tree of the ancient Iranians, the Haoma tree, produces the primal drink of immortality after which it is named. It is the first of all trees, planted in the fountain of life by the god Ormuzd. It is protected by ten fish, who keep a ceaseless watch upon a dragon sent by the evil god Ahriman, to destroy it.

The Bible describes the original home of humanity as a 'Garden of Delight' placed eastward in Eden. Of this it is written that in the midst of the Garden are to be found two trees; one is the Tree of Knowledge of Good and Evil and the other the Tree of Life. Of the former we are informed that in eating the fruit of it Adam and Eve defied God's Will and were consequently driven out of Paradise into a life of mortality and suffering; whereas, it is said of the Tree of Life, that whosoever eats of its fruit regains immortality – the never ending quest of mankind. It is then, not surprising that one of the principal conceptions in Kabbalistic thought is of the Tree of Life, as a macro and microcosmic model of creation." Marcus picked up a book that he had brought back with him when he returned from his break, opened it and passed it around the room, it contained various curious illustrations that appeared to be diagrammatic trees.

"There are many variations of the layout of the Tree of Life, the majority of which conform to an arrangement of ten spheres otherwise known as Sephiroth and twenty-two paths connecting them. The earliest description of the Sephiroth and the twenty-two paths first occurs in the *Sepher Yetzirah*, a text once attributed to the patriarch Abraham, but now thought to be the work of a great

The Rose Priory Dialogues

Jewish sage who lived in Palestine in the second century. It describes a metaphysical system that is deeply rooted in the astral religions of ancient Egypt and Mesopotamia. The following quotation from the *Sepher Yetzirah,* is often used as the basis for the Kabbalistic Tree of Life," Marcus picked up a little book and turned to a page that he had already marked, and began reading 'The Dweller in eternity, most high and holy – engraved his name by the three Sepharim – Numbers, Letters and Sounds. Ten are the ineffable Sephiroth. Twenty-two are the Letters, the Foundation of all things; there are Three Mothers, Seven Double and Twelve Simple letters. The ineffable Sephiroth are ten, as are the Numbers; and as there are in man five fingers over against five, so over them is established a covenant of strength, by word of mouth, and by the circumcision of the flesh. Ten is the number of the ineffable Sephiroth, ten and not nine, ten and not eleven. Understand this wisdom, and be wise by the perception.' Having finished reading Marcus put the book down.

"I'm absolutely certain that many of you will have struggled with that text, but now is not the time to explain it. It would take far too long. I read it to give you a flavour of an essential Kabbalistic text. However, if any of you still want to know more about it then talk to me on another day. I think this is a good time for us to stop, we've covered a lot of material and I don't know about you but I'm tired of talking. Go home and we'll continue next week" With that we gathered for a closing prayer and went our separate ways.

Part Five

Secrets Of The Tradition

The following week was an extremely busy one at work. I was collecting and delivering antiques all over the country and because of it I didn't get to meet or speak with any one at all, not even Leo, who worked for the same company. He, like me, was on the road most of the time, and didn't get home till late most evenings. I had a lot of time to myself and couldn't help reflecting on what Marcus had been introducing us to. It was a mind-blowing subject, that's for sure. I could see that he was taking it easy with us, yet I found it very difficult to keep up with him. In some ways I preferred the more easy going Marcus of a few weeks ago, on the other hand what he was teaching us was truly amazing. How long could this go on for? We shall find out soon enough I thought, in truth I can't wait.

One thing I found curious was when he looked at Leo, Ruth and I he seemed to know that we had arranged to question him. He seemed to be expecting Ruth's question and was ready for it. In fact he seemed to be silently saying "be careful what you ask for, because you might just get it and it might well be too much for you to handle". Anyway, I felt duty bound to rise to the challenge, and in some ways felt privileged to be involved.

Everyone was early and seated ready for the meeting. The room was alive with conversation about last week's meeting and it seemed that the air was buzzing with anticipation. Marcus arrived just on time and as usual began the meeting with a prayer. He then made the point that Kabbalah is such a vast subject that an in-depth exploration of the material it encompasses could never be addressed in one or two meetings such as this and that all we could hope to do was explore some of the fundamental building blocks of what is a very complex, multi-layered system of spiritual development. He continued, "I believe the last thing I said last week was that one of the primary tasks undertaken by a novice is the development of a metaphysical language that enables the soul to operate at a much higher level than our common vernacular allows. In part this begins with learning the Hebrew alphabet and all of the correspondences that go with it. It is not so much a foreign language that needs to be learnt as a mystical algebraic system, a system capable of many levels of permutation and interpretation. To the Kabbalist the letters of the Hebrew alphabet are more than simple components of words. The correspondences of each letter are very extensive; not only does every letter have a sound it also has a name, a numerical value and a form, all of which play a significant part in Kabbalah. Furthermore each letter has an associated image and an astrological symbol. For example, the letter Aleph has the value of 1, or, when written larger, the value of 1,000; It also corresponds with the image of an Ox and with the element of Air. The shape of the letter itself is said to describe a

Secrets Of The Tradition

Bull, and in some circles it is said to represent a man standing with his arms outstretched; at a high level Aleph symbolises the One, the Eternal and Omnipotent God. It is the principal channel between heaven and earth, and when considered as such it describes a flow of life between one and the other, thus some Kabbalists have likened it to Jacob's ladder. And before anyone asks, for those who want to know about Jacob's ladder see the twelfth book of Genesis.

The Kabbalist accepts as a matter of fact that the scriptures were given to man by Divine Inspiration; that they are the Word of God – the divine Will made manifest in the world of Man. Thus, the analysis of the sacred texts is taken very seriously; indeed, every sentence, every word and every letter is counted, compared and reflected upon; and because numbers also represent letters it is possible to establish the numerical value of any word or phrase. On this basis several systems of working with the letters have been established. These systems are very ancient and have proven to be invaluable tools for exploring the hidden depths of scripture.

This may seem strange, even obsessive to the majority of people who think numbers are simply tools for establishing quantity and value. Today, meaning in number rarely goes beyond dates of birthdays, anniversaries, lucky numbers etc., but in the ancient world number had a sacred import that would have been lost to humanity if it had not been preserved in societies of devoted scholars, and in the quiet sanctuaries of esoteric Schools. In our secularised world the mystical and symbolic interpretation of number is either associated with people in ancient history such as Pythagoras and his successors, or with periods of social decadence such as that of the Greco-Roman world of late antiquity. In our own time such interests are considered to be delusory and generally associated with the eccentrics who populate the fringes of our society.

However, it is a fact that throughout the ancient world the mystical significance of number was at least as important as its scientific application. But times have changed, and the mind of humanity is now focussed upon an exploration of the material world and the development of a material philosophy and science that excludes all that lies outside its perceived area of interest – including religion and all things connected with the life of the soul. This was probably inevitable, nevertheless the appreciation of the role that number plays in the spiritual dimension of human life has continued unabated from classical times, albeit in reduced circumstances; and nowhere has it been more appreciated than in the esoteric schools of the Diaspora that were eventually to give rise to the Kabbalists of the medieval era and beyond.

The spirit of scriptural interpretation aided by a metaphysical understanding of the meaning of number, has always been a key factor in the schools, and without an appreciation of this fact those who seek to engage in the work of Kabbalah will find themselves struggling to understand the different systems employed therein. The following notes about some of the key features of the classical world's perception of the meaning and philosophy of the basic numbers one to ten may thus be of value. Take notes if you want to, but I've printed out some sheets with the key information, as well as some of the trees you looked at last week. You will find them on the table by the front door." Marcus then read out the following:

Secrets Of The Tradition

"The number One emerges out of the Monad, which is the term used to express the principle of Unity. The Monad was understood by Pythagorean and Platonic philosophers to signify the first cause of creation, out of which emerges all things – including the number One, which in a paradoxical way is synonymous with the Monad but distinct from it. In nature it is the potential for diversity demonstrated in geometry by a point and in mathematics by the number One. As such it is the cause, source, beginning and basis of all number and numeration. They also understood that all even numbers were feminine and that all odd numbers were masculine except for the monad which is absolutely androgynous, because it is the father and mother of all number.

The number Two indicates division and polarisation. It is the first step from unity into diversity. The emergence of duality and diversification out of unity points to a polarisation of the number one and in doing so gives rise to contraries that can be expressed numerically. The number two signifies matter. In the Pythagorean tradition there are three stages of creation, the first is 'unity' symbolised by the Monad, the second is 'polarisation' into two opposite creative powers, symbolised by the Duad, the third is the uniting of these opposites in the generation of Life, symbolised by the Triad.

If we accept the number one as a point, and the number two as a line, then the number Three corresponds to the plane. The smallest plane imaginable is the triangle, which is the basis of the first three-dimensional figure – the three-sided pyramid. The number Three causes the potential of the monad to advance into actuality and extension and is therefore considered the basis of

Creation. It reconciles the polarities engendered through the actions of the number two; thus it has been called the number of 'friendship', 'harmony', 'peace' and 'unanimity'. It indicates a beginning, a middle and an end, and also implies a past a present and a future. Thus it speaks of form and time, of experience and knowledge. Out of these is born the world of duality, or in modern terms 'space-time'.

The number Four is considered to be the begetter of the Decad because the sum of all the numbers contained within it totals ten, (1+2+3+4). It is known as the 'foundation' because in geometrical procession it is the first number to display the nature of three-dimensional existence; point, line, plane, solid. Its form is considered to be the tetrahedron pyramid (the first solid) because it consists of four angles and four planes, and the cube because it is a three-dimensional square – the symbol of earth. The Tetrad gives rise to the four elements and universal existence, and as such signifies the quality and nature of change. It is understood that the monad applies to arithmetic, the dyad to music, the triad to geometry, and the tetrad to astronomy.

The number Five is thought to be androgynous, consisting as it does of the first masculine and feminine numbers (two & three) and because it was formed of male and female it was called 'marriage'. It was also understood to consist of the four elements plus Aether (spirit) and was therefore called 'lack of strife' because through the fifth element of spirit it reconciles any potential discordance. The pentad also signifies Justice because it governs equality in the soul and regulates providence, again through the element of Aether.

Secrets Of The Tradition

The number Six is thought to be the first perfect number because it arises out of the multiplication of the first even and odd numbers. It was also thought to be androgynous and to signify marriage because of the relationship between these two numbers (two & three). Because it was understood to be the form of forms, possessing wholeness, it was accepted as a symbol of the soul, and that the Universe was ensouled and harmonised by it, and through it attained wholeness, permanence, health and beauty. It signifies the six directions of extensions of solid bodies; up, down, forward, backward, left and right.

The number Seven is believed to be a virgin born neither of mother (even number) or father (odd number) but from the father of All (the monad). It was revered by the ancient philosophers, and called that which brings to completion. It was understood that all things, both in the heavens and upon the earth, were brought to completion by it, thus because it controlled mortal affairs it was called 'chance'. The soul is understood to descend into existence through the seven planetary spheres, acquiring its qualities or virtues from them. It also applied to the seven liberal arts and sciences, which were devised for the edification of the soul.

The number Eight was known to the ancient Platonic and Pythagorean philosophers as perfect harmony. The eighth sphere of the heavens – which was understood to contain the zodiac – encompassed all of the planetary regions, and as such has a particular significance concerning the harmony of the spheres, thus the number eight was considered to be the source of all musical ratios. Philolaus, a Pythagorean philosopher of the fifth Century BC, is attributed with the saying: "that after mathematical magnitude has become three-dimensional, thanks to the tetrad, there is quality and 'colour' of visible nature in the pentad, and ensoulment in the hexad, and intelligence and health and what he calls 'light' in the Hebdomad, and then next, with the Ogdoad, things come by love and friendship and wisdom and creative thought."

The number Nine is considered to be the greatest of all numbers within the Decad. It was also called the Perfector "because it gives completion to the fabrication of generation" (Proclus). As the end of a sequence of numbers it signifies the end of the formation of specific identities; for number admits nothing beyond the Ennead – returning as it does to the Monad in the Decad.

The number Ten, the Decad, is understood to signify the Universe because it is the most perfect boundary of number. It denotes the completion of building, bringing everything to fulfilment. It was called Eternity because it contains all things in itself. Thus it was recognised by the philosophers of the ancient world that there were ten heavenly spheres in which creation is contained. The Decad was venerated by the Pythagoreans as the tetraktys, a triangular representation of the combination of the first four numbers (1+2+3+4). It was also called fate because all numbers, things and events were sown into it."

Having read out the notes Marcus called time for a break and left the room. Everyone else seemed fascinated by the notes; the conversations taking place around the room were of nothing else. I sought out Marcus, who had just returned and found himself a cup of tea, and drew him aside, and asked him about the Kabbalistic system, about how essential it was to become expert in it. I was concerned that I would never be capable of doing such work. His response was surprising. He said that I shouldn't get lost in it, that the intellectual dimensions were in many ways a trap for the unwary and that I should always remember that we are on an inner journey of the soul, not the mind. He also made the point that as I was not a Jew I should not try to be a Jewish Kabbalist, if indeed I had any interest in being a Kabbalist at all. If I did, then I should understand that the Tradition was not to be ignored or treated lightly but to be understood in the light of my own culture. He also made the point that it is a life's work not a degree course. He shared these thoughts with me privately, although there was no suggestion of confidentiality. I was greatly relieved with the wisdom of his words and looked forward to hearing more.

Marcus returned to his seat and sat in silence, savouring his tea. Everyone else sat around chatting, the mood was really pleasant. Having finished his tea Marcus lightly tapped the side of his cup with a teaspoon signalling that the meeting was about to restart. Everyone settled down and Marcus continued, "Before the break I gave you a brief overview of number. It is far from exhaustive, but it will, perhaps, have demonstrated in some small way the reverence the philosophers of the ancient world had for the mystical significance of number, a reverence undoubtedly shared to some degree by many people of their day. Of course, it is probably true that much of society was then, as it is now, given over to common superstitions and vulgar practices, which at the collective level debases the profound spirituality and metaphysics underpinning the mystical appreciation of number. But, in the

The Rose Priory Dialogues

Kabbalistic schools this ancient knowledge was firmly tied to the spiritual exploration and understanding of the Torah; there never was room for idle speculation. Consequently, in Kabbalah the use of number has evolved into a powerful tool that opens up surprising dimensions in the understanding of the language of the scriptures and of certain ideas communicated therein.

The Torah is the 'Law', and it is expected that all true disciples should study the Law, to understand it as best they can. However, the written Torah is but a garment concealing a deeper meaning; this deeper meaning is known as the 'Soul of the Law', and it is to the Soul of the Law that the Kabbalist goes in search of Understanding. It is an interior journey wherein the soul reflects upon the significance of the Scriptures. To do this effectively the soul must direct and control the will. However, left to its own devices the will generally gravitates to the comfort zone of old and established behaviour patterns. In simple terms, the attention wanders, and it must be brought back to the main objective which is the study of the scriptures, wherein it may learn the way of the Divine and grow in understanding. Such work takes place in a state of meditation, and some of the most useful tools employed by the Kabbalist in meditation involve the symbolism of numbers and their correspondences.

Now many of you will have some understanding of meditation as we have already discussed it in previous meetings, however, you should know that for the Kabbalist meditation is a core discipline that enables the mind to be concentrated for considerable periods of time on a specific subject. For the Kabbalist that subject is the scriptures, the study of which is a profound engagement in meditation; and the most important tool in this engagement is a mind willing to engage in the work, supported by a clear conscience. To apply oneself effectively to the meditative exploration of scripture requires a lot of study and research, and, sufficient time to reflect upon the material contained therein; indeed, unrelenting attention and concentration is absolutely necessary if progress is to be made, because the interior path that leads the individual into the deep recesses of the soul, beyond the normal parameters of biology and psychology, does not reveal itself to an unfocussed mind. There is no easy path to proficiency in this kind of meditation, it is an art learned in the school of hard knocks; and much of the preliminary work of the Kabbalist is concerned with learning this art." Marcus paused and Ruth took the opportunity to say, "It seems that this is a path that few can take; it sounds like the curriculum for a devoted monastic, not for someone living in the world". "Quite so, Ruth, quite so; but many people, particularly the young, think they can engage with the more exciting aspects of Kabbalah and make a name for themselves – such enterprises often end in tears." "Do any people in the world make good Kabbalists" enquired Ruth, "Oh yes, certainly, in fact the majority of professed Kabbalists do live in the world, indeed, many of the more famous exponents of the Kabbalah were married and worked in partnership with their spouses, but they still tended towards living quiet lives, almost, but not quite, monastic.

It is probable that the earliest system of spiritual development in Israel took the form of emulating Moses' ascent of the sacred mountain of Sinai. This ascent is described in Exodus, the second book of the Pentateuch, which forms part of the oral tradition put into writing during the Babylonian captivity. It describes how the Jewish people, led by Moses, escaped from the land of Egypt. It is a narrative that may be read as an allegory concerning the passage of the soul out of the mundane world, which corresponds with the body and the animal nature. The Jewish enslavement in Egypt represents the bondage of the soul to the demands of the the mundane world. The Pentateuch consists of five books that among other things describe: the creation and fall of the soul; the wandering of the soul in the World; the soul's enslavement and liberation from Egypt; the soul's entry into the wilderness and its pilgrimage to the Holy mountain; Moses' ascent of the Holy Mountain; the covenant between God and mankind; the re-alignment of the soul with the Divine Law and the soul's entry into the promised land." Leo asked how one would go about exploring this story, how would we recognise the allegory if we had not been informed. Marcus surprised us all by pointing out that the term 'tradition' was not used accidentally, that students were introduced to the appropriate texts at the right time and that the tradition is actively passed on, not simply discovered; although people do stumble across them from time to time, but then the context is generally missing.

"Consider the outline I have just given to you, if you recall, a couple of weeks ago I described how the Creation could be understood in allegorical terms as the creation of the human soul, an immortal creature whose only vesture is a garment of pure spirit, or perhaps of light. In this state the soul exists within the 'Presence' of God, otherwise called Paradise, all of its needs being fulfilled in and by that Divine Presence. In this state time and space have no place as all souls share in the unity and omniscience of God. The 'fall', for whatever reason, is a movement out of that Presence, out of Unity, into duality. It describes a descent into the world of contending forces, where the soul experiences birth and death, pain and suffering, the needs of the flesh, and the need to work to survive; but worst of all separation from the Presence of God and the darkness of ignorance that comes with it. In this fallen state the soul knows nothing and has nothing, other than what the senses bring to it, hence the wandering of the people of Israel signifies the soul's growing awareness as it engages with the world through what it perceives via the senses, and to which it is driven by the incessant demands of the animal nature of the body. This animal or instinctive nature is by and large an unrelenting taskmaster and is symbolically represented as an embodiment of our carnal nature and appetites by Egypt (the world) and Pharaoh, (the personality). And thus the destiny of the soul would be irrevocably fixed if it were not for the influence of the Divine through the agency of Moses, who symbolises the human will that has touched, or has been touched by the heavenly realm, the 'Presence' of God. Thus inspired, the soul, discovering something of its true nature, is able to comprehend the limitations of the world of the senses, to overcome the instinctive nature (pharaoh), to gather the people (faculties), and withdraw them out of the immediate sphere of the instinctive nature.

The wilderness is a vastness found neither in heaven nor on earth. It is the great unknown that must be crossed, and is symbolised in all of the great epics quests and journeys from

Gilgamesh to the present." I asked Marcus who Gilgamesh was, and he replied, "Gilgamesh was a legendary king of ancient Sumer in Mesopotamia. Ancient tablets record an epic journey he undertook in search of immortality. It is a wonderful and compelling story that took him through the wilderness to the borders of the underworld, where he met Utnapishtim, the Sumerian Noah, who having survived the Deluge was, with his wife, granted immortality by the Gods. Utnapishtim eventually assisted Gilgamesh to find a sacred plant that would have given him the immortality he desired. However, he left it unattended and a serpent stole it away. Thus Gilgamesh fails and returns home.

Yet as interesting as the Epic of Gilgamesh may be, it is important that we understand that for the soul the wilderness is a vast astral region that is only accessed when it leaves the world of the senses. It is a treacherous and unpredictable realm in which many lose themselves but, the people of Israel were fortunate, they were led through the wilderness to the Holy Mountain of Sinai by a divine agent in the form of a pillar of fire by night and a pillar of smoke by day. Mount Sinai represents the high places of consciousness that the soul must ascend if it is to have any possibility of spiritual regeneration. Thus, Moses (the will) is called by God (inspired) to ascend the mountain (to the heavenly realms). It is an ascent in consciousness beyond the world of the senses, beyond the world of the imagination and even beyond the realm of abstract thought – into the Presence of God, who establishes a new covenant with the soul. This covenant is an interesting arrangement that requires of the soul that it recognizes and accepts the omnipresent unity of the Divine, that it turns away from investing the transient with power, and that it understands that all providence is from the Divine, and that there is no need to hold onto the desire for possessions. It is essentially an arrangement that requires of the soul that it re-aligns itself with Divine Law for only then will it be able to enter the Promised Land – the Presence of God – and fulfil its destiny. This broadly speaking is a Kabbalistic interpretation of the human condition set out in the five books of the Pentateuch.

The Kabbalah introduces the student to a much deeper meaning of these books than is commonly available; the contemplation of which enables the beginning of spiritual understanding, at the heart of which lies a teaching concerning the soul's path to freedom from the mundane world. This path is an interior journey into the depth of one's being; it is a difficult journey full of pitfalls, yet, when all is said and done, it is a path worth following, for at its terminus lies the emancipation of the soul. The beginning of this path is described in Exodus, under the following headings: The exodus of the Jewish people out of Egypt; their journey to the foot of Mount Sinai and the ascent of Mount Sinai by Moses."

"This is all very interesting" said Ivor, "but what is the soul, what do we mean by the word. I say this with all due respect because whenever I've discussed this with others, all that I get are fluffy answers; and not just from Christians, I've talked to people all over the world, from priests to paupers and no one has a clear answer. I suppose I'm asking you, what do you personally mean by the word soul?" Marcus smiled, closed his eyes for a moment, as he always does when thinking about a question, and then said,

The Rose Priory Dialogues

"there is no short answer to your question, it is important and deserves a lot of consideration, however, given the time constraints I can only answer you in the following way. A great deal of Kabbalistic doctrine is concerned in one way or another with the nature, experience and destiny of the soul. Yet, although many authors, both ancient and modern, have engaged with the psychology of the soul few have really explained what they actually mean by the word. Some refer to the soul in terms of it being an entity; that such and such a person is a young or old soul; others refer to it in terms of it being a vehicle: my soul is filled with joy or love; but still the question remains, what is meant by the term soul? The general consensus treats it as being the 'life-principle' by which we think, will, know and feel.

Some believe this principle is of an entirely non-material and spiritual nature, whilst others think of it as a material substance, a simple bye-product of the chemistry of matter. Some attribute to it immortality, others believe it to be no more than mortal. Some think of it as a simple undifferentiated creature incapable of division, whilst others see it as a creature of many parts. For example, the ancient Egyptians believed that a person possessed a physical body (Khat), and an immaterial double of the body known as the Ka. The Ka was also associated with the Ba, which was understood to reside within the heart. The Ka and the Ba dwelt in the tomb with the body, unable to wander away from it, and their continued existence depended upon offerings being made by family and friends of the deceased. The existence of the Ka and the Ba was understood to come to an end eventually when offerings ceased. The permanent life-giving principle was the Khu, a term

Secrets Of The Tradition

that means something like 'spirit-soul', whose nature was understood to be unchangeable, incorruptible and immortal. When the body died, it was possible to raise up from it, by means of religious ceremonies, a spirit-body called a Sahu, which the Khu would inhabit and enter heaven to live with Osiris and the blessed for all eternity.

In Hinduism the Sanskrit word for the soul is 'Atman', a word which means breath or wind – a correspondence that appears to be pretty well universal. The atman is regarded as a fragment or particle of the Divine, and as such is understood to have divine attributes; thus it is eternal, without magnitude and indestructible; similar in concept to the 'life-principle' described a moment ago. To the people of ancient Greece the soul was commonly known as Psyche, which besides meaning breath, life and spirit, also means butterfly or moth, a motif frequently used in ancient Greece as an metaphor for the immortal soul. In the late Hellenic world it was believed that the soul descended to earth from the heights of heaven, and that as it descended it was first clothed in an ethereal garment of non-material purity; as it continued its descent through the planetary spheres, it received first a solar garment then a lunar garment. Finally it was born into a physical body. Alternatively, the followers of Orpheus understood that man consisted of two distinct natures – a mortal, physical nature, derived from the Titans and an immortal spiritual nature derived from Dionysus. In ancient Greek mythology Dionysos was said to be the son of Zeus by Persephone. Zeus' wife, Hera, resented Dionysos and sought to destroy him. This was accomplished with the aid of her own children the Titans, who, with childish toys lured him away to a place of ambush, where they tore him apart and ate him. Upon discovering this heinous crime Zeus destroyed the Titans with his thunderbolts. They were burnt to ashes, and from these self-same ashes the race of Humanity sprang up. Human nature was then understood to consist of the dark destructive nature of the Titans, and the light creative and divine nature of Dionysos. The followers of Orpheus believed that the soul must free itself from this dualism by sublimating the passionate titanic nature and regenerating the divine Dionysian nature that lies within. In both cases the soul had to shed the garments of the body to realise its own pristine nature.

Among Christians the most popular view today is that Man consists of an immortal soul and a mortal body; not so different from the Late Greek really. Many Christian theologians maintain that a fully developed soul is infused into the embryo at conception. However, opinions concerning this do vary; the constitution and formation of the soul has been the subject of a long and continuing debate. In the first century, St. Paul taught that man consisted of a mortal terrestrial body, and an immortal celestial body; he wrote; "The first man was of the earth, made of dust; the second man is the Lord from heaven. As was the man of dust, so also are those who are made of dust; and as is the heavenly man, so also are those who are heavenly. And as we have borne the image of the man of dust, we shall also bear the image of the heavenly Man." And before anyone asks, you will find this text in the New Testament, I Corinthians, chapter 15. In the first half of the third Century, Origen, a famous mystic and theologian taught that the soul existed in heaven before Adam, and before descending into the world; that its imprisonment in a physical body was the result of a primeval fall from grace; and that the resurrection will not involve a physical body. Against this, Tertullian, another theologian, argued that souls were contained in Adam, and that they were passed on to children from their parents in an act of material generation. Augustine held a similar opinion except for him the generation was a spiritual generation. This doctrine is known as Traducianism.

Medieval philosophers, as exemplified by Thomas Aquinas in the thirteenth century, understood the soul to be composed of a spiritual substance, and that it incarnated in three progressive stages of development, vegetative, sensitive and rational. The first, the vegetative stage, corresponds with conception and the earliest development of the embryo; the second, the sensitive stage, emerges as the embryo develops; and the third, the rational stage, manifests as the embryo reaches maturity in the womb and completes the process of incarnation. These stages are consistent with Aquinas' assertion that three things are to be found in spiritual substances, Essence, Power and Operation.

It is a notion that is comparable with the Hypostases of Neoplatonic thought, where Essence corresponds with the One, Power with Nous and Operation with the World Soul. Indeed, the influence of Neo-Platonism found in the doctrines of medieval Kabbalah is in keeping with the doctrines taught in many esoteric Christian circles. This doctrine can be traced back to the teachings of Plato, who maintained that all souls existed before incarnating in a body, and that they exist for all eternity. Similar ideas are also expressed in Kabbalistic thought, which maintains that the soul was formed before the beginning of the world, hidden in the

Divine; as the process of creation began souls were brought forth into the upper paradise and stored in a great 'Treasure-house' (Binah), from whence they progressed into this world.

Over the course of time Jewish thought has expressed many different views on the nature and destiny of the soul. The classical and most enduring view is that of the Resurrection; which is the belief that at the end of the age the dead will be revived by God, complete with their bodies, to live again on earth. The Biblical view of the Resurrection is best summed up in Daniel 12: 2-3, were it says: "And many of them that sleep in the dust of the earth shall awake, some to everlasting life and some to reproach and everlasting shame. And the wise shall shine as the brightness of the firmament and some of the many righteous as the stars for ever and ever." This doctrine encapsulates two basic conceptions; the unity of body and soul and a moral dimension that determines the nature of post-resurrection existence. However, the Bible is not absolutely clear about the posthumous fate of the soul – the most distinct view expressed being that the soul descends into a kind of Hades or Hell called Sheol, wherein it leads a vague ethereal and shadowy existence. During the time of the Second Temple, the concept of an immortal posthumous existence in the heavenly realms arose, competing with the more traditional concept of the resurrection of the dead. Eventually, the belief in the immortality of the soul became a fundamental principle of both the Jewish and Christian Faiths.

In the Talmudic period the Rabbis generally taught that the soul was separable from the body; separating during sleep to draw nourishment from the spiritual realms and, at death, leaving the body only to be reunited with it again at the Resurrection. At the same time some of the rabbis taught that after death a righteous soul entered the Garden of Eden and that wicked souls went to eternal damnation in hell; or that righteous souls ascended upwards, to be gathered into the 'Treasury', while wicked souls were cast back upon the earth – in other words they were subject to reincarnation; opinions about this have differed from time to time, and place to place.

It should be noted that among medieval Kabbalists the teachings concerning reincarnation or transmigration were quite narrow and generally confined to specific circumstances. Not every soul was subject to transmigration, but only those for whom it was absolutely necessary. It was taught that the righteous – those who had fulfilled their obligations as Jews – had no need to re-incarnate, whereas, the majority of souls, those who had failed in their obligations, and were therefore to some degree sinners, became subject to the process of transmigration. The incorrigibly wicked, alas, were to be condemned to the fires of Hell. It was also taught that the number of incarnations was generally limited to three, a notion clearly drawn from the Book of Job, where it states: "Behold, God works all these things twice, in fact three times with a man to bring back his soul from the Pit that he may be enlightened with the light of life." However, it was also understood that the Zaddikim, which means 'Righteous Ones', were souls sent by God. It was understood that they could re-incarnate many times for the benefit of the world. Kabbalistic doctrine maintains that the soul is a spiritual entity whose origin is divine and whose immortal nature is an incontrovertible fact, and that it incarnates in the world only to fulfil a specific task; the fulfilment of which enables it to engage in a many-staged ascent to its primal dwelling place. This ascent begins with the soul attaining entrance to the earthly paradise, from where it begins its ascent. The teaching concerning the soul's role in this work is central to Kabbalism.

Although the soul is essentially one thing it may be divided into several distinct parts. This is clearly demonstrated in the Zohar where the prevailing view is that the soul consists of three parts; the Nephesh, Ruach and Neshemah. The term Nephesh, refers to the part of the soul that is associated with the body and all of those things connected with sustaining our physical being throughout life. It is not the body itself, but the lowest expression of the spiritual life of the soul. Its nature is to fulfil the needs of the flesh and to preserve it from harm; it is appetitive and driven to survive at all costs. It has no light or energy of its own but receives its sustenance from the Ruach. The term Ruach refers to the faculty of consciousness associated with the principle of rational thought. It is through the Ruach that the soul is sustained by the power of the Nephesh. If the life force of the Ruach were to be withdrawn then death would ensue because the Nephesh would be unable to maintain itself in the body. The Ruach corresponds with the spiritual body, but in most of humanity it is a spiritual body subject to the vicissitudes of the passionate nature. The term Neshemah refers to the spiritual faculty of the soul. It is the sovereign reason within us, which is the true spiritual intellect above the rational mind. It is hewn from the source of life and from the well-spring of intelligence and wisdom. That all exist as part of one thing is unquestionable, but few in this world are able to take advantage of the powers of all three. It is said that every soul is conscious at the level of Nephesh; however, it is taught that if it is used well, to its highest potential, then consciousness of the Ruach is bestowed upon the soul. If the soul is also able to use the Ruach to its highest purpose then the divine Godhead exalts the soul, bestowing upon it the crown of Neshemah, which is the objective of all true seekers since it is through the power of the Neshemah that the Ruach is emancipated from the shackles of the mundane world and thus able to realise its true spiritual nature. Other names attributed to it are the Higher Self, the Overself, and the Holy Guardian Angel of the Soul.

From both a Jewish and a Christian Kabbalistic perspective the soul is in a fallen state and must rise out of it; this is the principal work of the Kabbalist – to regenerate and reintegrate the soul; both of the individual and of humanity itself. The first step in achieving this objective, as is the primary work of spiritual aspirants everywhere, lies in undertaking the work of self-improvement, whereby one may participate in the great work of spiritual regeneration. In the Christian mysteries, the path of the soul's spiritual perfection may be understood as consisting of seven stages, thus: 1) Purification of the senses, appetites and desires; 2) Control of the tongue; 3) Examination & Purification of Conscience; 4) Prayer; 5) Meditation on the maxims of Faith; 6) Development of Virtue; and finally 7) Frequent Communion. It is no different for initiates in any other Faith or philosophy. Indeed, the same kind of work is undertaken by the apprentice freemason, who is likened to a rough stone freshly taken from the quarry, and who must be shaped into the perfect cube before he is fit for use in the construction of the Temple – the metaphor being that until his mind and nature are sufficiently refined he will be unable to engage in the spiritual work. The same may be recognised in the labours of the initiates of the Mystery Schools of the Greco-Roman world. Before undertaking the Cathartic Rites, they must first develop the civic virtues, moderating their passions and learning to live in Harmony with society. These same virtues Prudence, Fortitude, Justice and Temperance, are also the basis for the essential work of spiritual regeneration.

So, Ivor, as you may gather, the subject is a complex one requiring a great deal of study. From my own perspective I am happy to think of the soul as the immortal-life principle in everyone, I'm equally happy to think of it as an entity and as a vehicle, because to me it is all of these things, but the important question right now is have I answered your question?" Ivor sat for a moment, a little bemused, then said to Marcus, "I think you have, I think you've given me a great deal to think about and I would really like to talk with you privately about this as I don't know what to say at this point; I've more questions going through my mind now than before; thank you very much." Marcus nodded, he didn't say anything, I guess he understood Ivor's predicament. What more could he say, indeed, we were all quite speechless. How many of us had actually thought about the soul beyond our intuitive perceptions of a sense of self. I know I hadn't, and by the look on everyone's face neither had they. I felt really thick and stupid, but I consoled myself with the thought that he didn't expect any of us to follow in his footsteps but to find our own path, and that he was only helping us to do just that.

The meeting came to an end shortly after, and as usual we closed with a prayer. It seemed to me that Marcus's prayer was always extempore and relevant to the moment, yet he always seemed to bring through a sense of the numinous. I had been brought up with prayers being read from a book, parrot fashion; from the first time I met Marcus I have never stopped wondering how he does it. Did he learn them off by heart, then if so who taught him? I suppose probably I will never find out. The group dispersed in good spirits although the chatter was more subdued than usual.

Before parting company I arranged to meet with Ruth at the Café the following day. Leo and Louise said that they would try and join us if they could. We agreed to meet about two o'clock. I dropped off Leo and Louise and went home to my bed with a great deal to think about.

Part Six

A Mystery Unfolds

Saturday started as a grey, wet and blustery day, but by lunchtime a blue sky had emerged, the wind had dropped and the temperature had risen considerably; so, rather than take the car, I walked down to the café enjoying the day as I went. I got there a little before two o'clock; the others had yet to arrive. The place was quite busy, and the low hum of people quietly chatting suggested all was well with the world. When I entered the café I panicked for a moment, thinking I might not find a table, but as luck would have it an empty table was waiting just for me. I ordered a coffee, found a newspaper and sat down.

   I looked around taking stock of the patrons of the establishment, many of whom were clearly regulars. I'm sure most of them are involved in esoteric things; I'd been in similar places all over the world, from the USA to India, places where people check you out, looking to see if you are of the 'faith', as it were, although I'm not convinced you can tell if someone is a spiritual or mystical person merely by how they dress and walk. Anyway, this place had an atmosphere about it I rather liked; which is why I came here. It wasn't the place itself that generated the atmosphere, it seemed to emanate from the collective consciousness of its customers, all of whom radiated in one way or another their interest in what you might call 'newage' subjects. I suspect on certain days, like today for example, being a Saturday, this café filled up with a selection of magicians, sorcerers, shamans, healers, witches and a few astrologers etc. I mused about how dangerous entering this place on such days could be, particularly for unwary customers who would unwittingly run a gauntlet of psychic interrogation, during which their auras would be checked out, their minds read, and the unconscious messages of body language understood. I imagined that occasionally wills would clash and Hexes would fly invisibly across the room only to be disarmed in mid-air; yet to the casual observer the place was full of quiet self-conscious people enjoying conversation or engrossed in their books.

Daydreaming, I sat looking out of the window savouring my coffee and waiting for the others to show. In my reverie it occurred to me that no one had ever asked Marcus about the history of the Order he belonged to, or about the ancient history of the Rose Priory. Were there really tunnels and caves underneath it? It would be amazing if there were. I was imagining what they might contain when Leo arrived. He was alone. I asked him if he knew anything about the subterranean warren of tunnels and caves that were rumoured to exist below the Priory. He thought that he had heard such rumours but couldn't remember where. "Its odd, isn't it," he said, "how often we think we know something, yet can't recall where we first learnt about it." "Leo, you know I've been going to the Priory only for a few weeks yet, my memory is as befuddled as

A Mystery Unfolds

yours; I must have heard it from someone or another in the last few weeks, but from who? It's very frustrating."

We both sat in silence thinking about where we might have acquired such knowledge, when Ruth and Louise turned up. They ordered drinks at the bar, green tea I think, and sat down. "You two look lost in thought", Louise said cheerfully, "We were just thinking about where we first heard about the caves and tunnels under the Priory," Leo said, "In fact" he continued, "Neither of us can recall anything, its becoming a bit of a mystery." "It sounds really exciting, let me in on it," interrupted Ruth, "And me" echoed Louise, "I don't have any idea what you are talking about." All I could say was, "Leo, it's down to you as you seem to be the only one here who knows anything." I grinned at the expression on his face reflecting his growing realisation of being set up. "Well....." he said feigning on an atmosphere of mysteriousness, "I've heard that the current Priory is built on the ruins of a much older building, possibly medieval. Rumour has it that there has been a religious house on this site from the earliest times, even as far back as the Roman occupation and that there is a warren of tunnels and caves under the Priory, carved out over the centuries by members of the Order. That's all I know really." "How do we find out more" said Louise, "I'm absolutely enthralled by the idea. What do you think Ruth?" Ruth didn't answer immediately, she just looked thoughtfully into the distance, then with a start she said, "Why don't we go down to the Central Library and do some research in the archives, they're bound to have some records concerning the place, even if it's nothing, if you see what I mean. That is, if there is something then we have a good starting point, but if we find nothing, we can probably be sure that it's only a legend, a folk tale without any substance, no?" On that note we finished our drinks and walked down to the Central Library, which wasn't that far away. En route we discussed who would do what in the library. Leo agreed to look up any geological information; Louise and Ruth agreed to check out the city and county archives, and I agreed to look for anything on religious houses. We agreed to meet at five o'clock on the green outside the cathedral.

I quickly discovered a book about the religious and monastic orders of England, in which I found a reference to there being a monastic settlement on the site of the Rose Priory in the eleventh century, and possibly earlier, as it was listed in the Doomsday Book. I also discovered that during the Dissolution of the Monasteries, which took place in the mid-sixteenth century, it was seized by agents of Henry VIII; but in the late seventeenth century was given back to the Order to be used as a hospital, although not as a monastic house. In the early eighteenth century it caught fire and lay in ruins for half a century or more, but then it was rebuilt in the 1760's, by brothers of the Order. Louise and Ruth reported that the earliest records in the archives indicated that a religious house had been on the site.

They also quoted the Domesday book, and an obscure reference attributed to the sixteenth century, which said that in olden times the monks of this establishment used to sleep underground and that they were rumoured to practice arcane rites in the caves and that they also had a great library hidden in a secret cave beneath the Priory. If they did no-one ever found it, although many had looked for it, including King Henry's agents. Leo reported that the ground was essentially Limestone, a fact that supported the possibility of naturally formed caves. "Well, what I want to know, assuming there are caves under the Priory, is how we get down there?" said Ruth excitedly. "Do you think Marcus will help us?" Louise asked in a doubtful way. "There must be a way!" affirmed Leo, then concluded "but I think we first need to do more research."

I thought this was all very exciting and definitely worth pursuing. We all agreed to try in our own way to persuade Marcus to tell us more about it and if possible let us see the caves system for ourselves. It was a very excited group of people that parted company, each of us speculating to ourselves all kinds of fantastic possibilities. All through the week I could think of nothing else. The time flew by and before I knew it Friday was upon us.

Marcus was late. Leo, Ruth and I stood close to the fire talking. "Do you think we will be talking about Kabbalah tonight?" "I hope so," said Leo, "It must be the system he works with" said Ruth, "Only a part of it, I think he said", Leo corrected her. "Do you think he's psychic?" I muttered, "Is the Pope a Catholic?" Ruth laughed, "Honestly, Joe, how can you ask such a question, he's been running rings around us ever since we proposed interrogating him, what a silly question." Leo laughed, "I have to agree, he seems to know exactly what anyone thinks, almost before they do." We all agreed that the best time to talk to Marcus about the rumours concerning the tunnels was after the meeting, as it wouldn't really be appropriate to highjack the meeting for such a subject.

The Rose Priory Dialogues

Marcus arrived a few minutes later and the meeting began with Patrick asking him why he, a professed Christian, was a Kabbalist, which is Jewish. "You know, Patrick, your question is very interesting, the truth is simply that every member of the Order is expected to make a study of comparative religions and philosophies. So my studying a Jewish metaphysical system is not really as strange as you might think, after all Christianity did grow out of Judaism; but I must also say that your question suggests to me that you are missing the point. The word Kabbalah means 'tradition', let us be in agreement about that one thing; with that in mind I suggest that you stop thinking that Kabbalah is a Jewish tradition only, instead, think of it as a timeless and universal tradition that has been passed down from the ancient world to ours. Jewish mystics preserved a great deal of this tradition, whereas the Christian Church only preserved some of it. I'm interested in Kabbalah because I am a Christian, not in spite of my Christianity. It is not Judaism that lies at the heart of Kabbalah, but spiritual regeneration, which is universal and timeless; and as for being psychic, maybe I am, but on the other hand perhaps you're all just too obvious." Marcus chuckled to himself at the look on our faces, then he closed his eyes and became very still; in fact every one and every thing became very still, almost like the silence of falling snow. Even the fire and the clock seemed be affected. The atmospheres he seemed to generate at will were like nothing on earth I'd ever experienced. They weren't in your face or eventful, quite the opposite in fact, they were moments of deep peace that brought a sense of healing and contentment to the soul – an ethereal balm. How long we sat in that silence I'll never know,

A Mystery Unfolds

hours in soul time I guess, but probably minutes in real-time. At some point Marcus continued speaking: "That's better, there's far too much mental static in here tonight," he looked straight at Leo and myself, a wide grin on his face; "I suspect some of you have had an overdose of irrelevant cerebral activity in recent days; it can give you bad headaches if you're not careful." With that he became a little more serious and continued, "You know, there's a vast amount of material involved in Kabbalah; in truth, any one small area could keep a student occupied for a lifetime or more, but, one area you should be mindful of is the subject of 'Practical Kabbalah', which many today believe deals with ceremonial and talismanic magic. However, Magic and Practical Kabbalah don't necessarily mean the same thing to a traditional student of the Kabbalah as they do to many aspiring magicians. Indeed, to the Kabbalist Practical Kabbalah is an exercise in practical mysticism rather than an exercise in magic. This distinction is important, because for the Kabbalist the central teachings of Kabbalah are the scriptures, and therein much of what is called magic is forbidden. In the Book of Deuteronomy it states; "There shall not be found among you anyone who practises witchcraft, or a soothsayer, or one who interprets omens or a sorcerer or one who conjures spells, or a medium or a spiritist or one who calls up the dead. For all who do these things are an abomination to the Lord." Not a popular text today, yet many traditional Kabbalists would denounce the common understanding of Practical Kabbalah on this passage alone. Nevertheless, Practical Kabbalah has attracted the attention of so many aspiring magicians today that the words 'Kabbalah' and 'Magic' have become synonymous."

The Rose Priory Dialogues

Several people attempted to speak but Patrick's voice won the dayt. "I've read a lot about magic, but I'm still at a loss about what it means; is there a simple definition of magic, because if there is I have yet to find it?" "Patrick, your question has vexed clever minds for centuries. Why? Perhaps it is because the word 'Magic' has meant, and continues to mean, many things to many people; it has been the subject of debate for so long yet there is no consensus as to its meaning. Indeed the meaning of the word has been a matter of uncertainty since classical times. What is known is that the word Magic is generally thoght to originate from the Greek 'mageia', a word that the Greeks derived from the word Magu or Magi, a title of the sacerdotal caste of ancient Persia and Media, who were followers of the prophet Zoroaster and priests of the god Ahuramazda. The word Magi signifies those who are 'wise', not only in the ways of the world, but also in the ways of God, and because of their wisdom the Magi commanded great respect throughout the ancient world. Plato, felt comfortable using them as exemplars of the highest virtue when discussing statesmanship in Alcibiades I, where he describes how a royal prince of ancient Persia, upon reaching the age of fourteen years, was put in the care of four carefully selected magi. These masters were reputed to be the best among the Persians; one of them being the wisest, another the most just, the third the most temperate, and the fourth the most valiant. Thus Plato held the Magi in the highest esteem, and furthermore, informs us that the work of a magus, or magician, is the worship of the gods (Theurgy).

The Classical world came to an end with the collapse of the Western Roman Empire in the fifth century, followed by the Dark

A Mystery Unfolds

Ages and the medieval era, throughout which magic generally fell under three main headings: Natural Magic, Goëtia, and Theurgy. Natural Magic is concerned with the hidden workings of nature; its properties, powers, qualities, substances and virtues. It was held to be the noblest part of the physical sciences, and as such was not forbidden by the Church and therefore not legislated against. For many students of the magical art it was the consummation of Natural Philosophy. The study of Alchemy, Medicine, Astrology, and the manipulation of nature's 'finer forces' were the proper domain of Natural Magic. One of its greatest exponents was Paracelsus, a renowned healer of the sixteenth century who became famous for his Doctrine of Signatures, in which he proposed that natural objects suggest by their external appearance the complaints for which they were cures; thus, some plants may be seen as representing parts of the body, whilst others suggest diseases for which they may be used as remedies. A 'signature' was therefore any distinctive feature or quality that indicated a connection between remedy and malady. Natural Magic was understood to be the application of true and natural causes to produce rare and unusual effects by means that were neither superstitious nor diabolical. It follows then, that there is a fundamental distinction between the field of Natural Magic and those of Goëtia and Theurgy, for Natural Magic does not involve engaging with spirits or gods, be they good or bad; rather, it is a discipline of enquiring into the workings of Nature, whereas Goëtia and Theurgy are essentially magical disciplines that do engage with spirits and gods, and indeed, with a vast hierarchy of other supernatural beings.

The Rose Priory Dialogues

The terms sorcerer, witch and witchcraft, were known to the ancient Greeks by the name Goës or Goëtes, from whence the term Goëtia and Goëtic are derived. Indeed, from the earliest times the term Goëtia has been employed in a sinister and disreputable sense. It has invariably been linked with magical ceremonies devised to control and manipulate spirits for dubious reasons, often to the detriment of others. Today Goëtia is usually associated with the seventeenth century Grimoire, *The Lesser Key of Solomon*, around which a vast amount of fanciful myth and legend has accumulated. Indeed, Goëtia has long been considered to be synonymous with Black Magic. Historically, Goës (sorcerers, witches etc.) were often seen as a threat to the social order and there were many occasions when the laws against them were vigorously enforced, particularly in the pre-Christian world of the Roman Empire.

Almost from the beginning of its existence Rome had laws against the exponents of sorcery and witchcraft. The earliest Roman code of Law, the 'Twelve Tablets', introduced in the mid fifth century BC, so named because they were publicly displayed in the Forum on twelve tablets of Bronze, forbade people from using magic to harm others, the punishment for such a crime being severe. In the first century BC the Patrician Sulla, reformed these laws, making it very clear that any person who celebrated, or caused to be celebrated, impious or nocturnal rites, so as to enchant, bewitch, or bind anyone, should be crucified, or thrown to wild beasts, and that persons addicted to the art of magic, were to be thrown to wild beasts, or crucified. Magicians themselves were to be burned alive. No one was permitted to possess books on

A Mystery Unfolds

the art of magic, and any found in possession of them were to be publicly burnt, and those who possessed them, after being deprived of their property, if they were of superior rank were to be deported to an island, and those of inferior station put to death, for not only was the practice of magic prohibited, but also the knowledge of the same.

Obviously, the ancient world was no bed of spiritual roses, for society then, just like today, had its share of unscrupulous people who were prepared to use both natural and supernatural forces to take advantage of, and or intimidate their neighbours. However, in Plato or Sulla's time it would have been unlikely that a sorcerer or witch could have been mistaken for a member of the Magi, for the Magi, whether from Persia, ancient Egypt, Greece or Rome, were the elite of their civilisation. They were extremely learned, not only in spiritual sciences such as Theology and Psychology, but in all of the known empirical sciences, including Astronomy, Mathematics, Metallurgy, Philosophy, Medicine and Physiology, and as such were highly respected. As Plato so eloquently put it, the work of the Magi was the worship of the Gods; work that is formally known as Theurgy.

The word 'theurgy' is based upon the Greek words Theos (God) and Ergos (work), from which is derived the word theourgia – which means 'works of God' or 'divine workings'. These divine workings were sacramental rites or mysteries central to the spiritual life of the ancient world. Over the centuries these ancient rites were absorbed into, and became important features of the sacramental system of the Church. Alas, in more recent times they have been discarded; being no longer valued either by the Church or the State. Now, I think it could be said that our culture has barely any knowledge of the sacred rites of spiritual regeneration that were so important to the ancient world. This is hardly surprising as the secular world generally sees the spiritual dimension of life as a pot-pourri of primitive beliefs, practices and superstitions promoted by the unscrupulous with the intention of fleecing the naive and the incredulous, or, by the misguided and the irrational as a delusory pseudo-science that rests more on hopes, dreams and misconceptions than on any objective truth or observation. Even the majority of those who are knowledgeable perceive Theurgy and Goetia to be by and large one and the same thing; a potentially hazardous perception as the objectives and dynamics of both are very different, indeed, on their own terms they are diametrically opposed.

Eliphas Levi, a 19th century French occultist, said of Goetic Magic: "This torrent of universal life….it is this which brings to our evocations and to the conjurations of our Goëtic Magic such swarms of larvæ and phantoms. Therein are preserved all the fantastic and fortuitous assemblages of forms which people our nightmares with such abominable monstrosities." With these words Levi illustrates the distinction between Goëtia and Theurgy, for in Goëtia the magician seeks to control the forces of nature and the spirits that abound in creation, to take heaven by storm, to become as a god; 'Let my Will be done' is the rule, whereas the Theurgist seeks purification, liberation, and salvation of the soul, following a path of 'Thy Will be done' as opposed to 'My Will be done'. This is best summed up by Iamblichus, who wrote in the third century: "From the beginning, it is necessary to divide ecstasy into two species: one is turned towards the inferior, filled with foolishness and delirium, but the other imparts goods more honourable than human wisdom. The former is unstable, the latter unchangeable; the first is counter to nature, the latter is beyond nature; the former makes the soul descend, the latter raises it up; and while the former entirely separates the soul from participation in the divine, the latter connects the soul with the divine. It is obvious then that describing what is meant by 'Magic' is at best a little tricky.

If magic has meant different things to different people at different times, there is nevertheless a common theme that runs throughout the history of magic; that theme is control. In all systems of magic throughout history, people have sought to control their material and spiritual environment, and all things in it. In material terms such mysticism is seen in today's world as a delusory pseudo-science, and so it might be, but in spiritual terms magic is a term for the inevitable technology that derives from theology. However, as we have seen, there is magic and there is magic. Broadly speaking, Natural Magic was traditionally concerned with exploring the natural world, and over the course of time has naturally evolved into the modern sciences, but there is a system of magic that falls neither under the banner of 'Divine Workings' nor under the banner of the diabolical.

In Kabbalah the Divine Workings are not magic and the Kabbalist is neither a magician nor seeks to become a magician. It may be difficult for an impartial observer to grasp the significance of this point, but it will become clear if one understands that to the Kabbalist Practical Kabbalah is concerned only with the Divine

The Rose Priory Dialogues

Names of God as derived from the Scriptures and their mysterious workings as unfolded in Kabbalistic processes. The Divine Names are intimately connected with the Sephirotic world and its emanation, thus, to engage with the Divine Names is to engage in a sacred rather than a magical process. For the Kabbalist this system constitutes the essence of Practical Kabbalah."

Someone I had not seen before, a woman of indeterminate age, she could have been anywhere between mid fifties to mid-seventies, spoke out, "Hello, my name is Ann, this is my first visit and I am having trouble keeping up with you, I would be grateful if you were to let me know what the "Sephirotic World" is, what does it mean" A few others murmured in agreement with her. Marcus, fell silent, as he usually did, then said, "The Sephirotic World is the spiritual basis of creation; and the Sephiroth are the divine archetypes that serve as patterns for the entire cosmos. It is a realm far beyond the comprehension of this world, although it is possible for the soul to enter into it, but only when purified of the stuff of this world. However, there are some who think that it is possible through magical means to manipulate the Sephirotic world to suit their own ends. Such people fall under the heading of magicians and sorcerers, which was the point we were discussing a moment ago. To the Kabbalist, such processes, which are central to Practical Kabbalah are geared only to the regeneration of the soul, not to its elevation, aggrandisement, or for intellectual curiosity.

Studying Kabbalah is no lightweight undertaking. Although its outer skin, by which I mean the glyphs of the Tree of Life, the

A Mystery Unfolds

Four Worlds and the Alphabet, with all of their correspondences, may serve well even the most casual dabbler in esoteric workings, it is not a path suited to those with a casual interest or dilettante attitude. It is, after all is said and done, a central part of the Mysteries most suited to those souls whose love of the Spirit is greater than their love of the world; indeed, its inner sanctuaries are only accessible to those who are brave enough to give up the world, to leave the herd, as it were: for things divine are not attainable by those who comprehend the body alone, but only by those who 'Stripped of their garments arrive at the summit.'"

Ann, I later found out, was the chief executive of a well-known complementary medical centre devoted to the care of those suffering from cancer. said "I think I follow what you are saying, but what do you mean by the words 'stripped of their garments', is this a metaphor or are they to be understood literally?" Marcus replied, "No, Ann, it is not to be understood literally; the garments referred to here are bodies that we wear like layers of clothing. They have been described at different times and by different authors in various ways, some speak of them as etheric and astral bodies, others refer to them as subtle bodies, many refer to them as sheaths or vehicles. All of them allude to an understanding that the human vehicle we call a body does not only consist of different systems such as the arterial, digestive and nervous systems, but also consists of several unique elements or bodies that are incorporated within and about the physical frame. Each body is of a different density and frequency of vibration. Thus one model proposes a physical body, an electro-magnetic body and a body of light each contained within the other – the physical within the etheric and the etheric within the body of light; a bit like Russian dolls. There are many models and definitions concerning the nature and arrangement of these bodies, but it matters little what they are called, whether they be sheaths, bodies, vehicles or indeed garments, they all amount to the same thing in the end – fields of human experience.

To identify these "garments" is an important part of the work of a Kabbalist, not simply to know that they exist and give them labels, but to actually perceive them for what they are and what they do – to have direct knowledge of them. However, the work of identification is a slow process; it is more a growth in understanding, than identifying a specific object or event. To perceive the activities of the etheric is to see the Nephesh in action, but it is not with the eyes that it is perceived, but with the inner eye of an attentive and reflective mind. What follows is frequently an uncomfortable but necessary education as the soul slowly modifies its conduct, and consequently the nature of the Nephesh. In the schools this education comes under the heading of the virtues, particularly the 'civic virtues', which are Courage, Justice, Temperance and Prudence. To the casual or immature observer these virtues may suggest moral integrity, or qualities of one who follows the herd, but to the wise they are the insignia of a soul growing strong in the light of self-knowledge; they are indeed outward expressions of inner qualities that are quintessentially spiritual."

"Yes, I see what you mean", Ann responded, "I have always been puzzled by the concept of virtue, what it actually means, is it a thing, something substantial, or is it a quality? I've never really been able to be sure. Indeed, I've never really grasped what society understands by it apart from it being, as you say, another word for the moral integrity of someone or other. You speak of it differently; tell me, where do people such as myself find such information?" Marcus looked at Ann, closed his eyes and sat in silence for a moment. He then looked up and said, "The subject is subtle and perhaps too profound for a discussion such as this, but I'll try to explain my understanding of the subject in line with the teaching I was given. You may or may not know that the will of God is manifest in creation as Divine Law, to which everything in creation conforms. Divine Law is perceived in the natural world, the world we live in, through the laws of Nature; in short Divine Law is known to humanity through Natural Law. Furthermore, the will of God is expressed in all things as the will 'to be', the unfolding of which conforms to Natural Law. You may recall we touched upon this subject some weeks ago. When I was a novice this concept proved to be very difficult to understand. However, the analogy my teacher provided for me to meditate upon was that of light, which travels from the sun to earth, where it is absorbed within the atmosphere and substance of the earth, and in which the whole cycle of life as we know it begins. Without it there would be no photosynthesis and probably no manifestation of life as we know it. Light, then, is analogous with life itself, and its nature is non-material, that is to say, spiritual; furthermore, its natural disposition, as I said earlier, is to evolve a form through which it may perfectly express its full potential, and whereby it may eventually transcend material existence. Porphyry has a great deal to say about this in his treatise, *The Principles of the Theory of the*

The Rose Priory Dialogues

Intelligibles, where he discusses the development of virtue as the foundation of purification and self-knowledge. According to Porphyry, it is only through this process that the soul can realise that it is of a very different nature to the flesh and by the appropriate actions may transcend that flesh.

I was taught that although in principle we are spiritual beings we are nevertheless born in the world and of the world; and that our nature, instincts, appetites and faculties correspond with our level of evolution, and as such we are absolutely in harmony with natural law. Consequently, when we act in accord with our nature we are true to ourselves. However, the divine imperative to 'become' requires that we develop and refine our nature, unfolding the divine potential that lies within us. With this in mind we may understand virtue to be a recognisable manifestation of the divine nature unfolding within us, furthermore, virtue is not only to be seen in ourselves but in all life forms. Indeed, in some life- forms, we may see virtue as being singular, in others we may see several virtues as the divine essence unfolds and reveals itself in different ways.

When I was a novice I meditated upon the virtues, thinking of them as nuggets of gold shining in the dirt, At some point in my reflections I realised that although they appeared to be unique items of treasure they were in reality manifestations of a great seam of gold hidden in the earth, breaking through here and there to remind us of the presence of the source of life hidden behind. So it is with virtue, the manifestation of which, be it one virtue or many, indicates the emerging presence of the infinite and eternal Godhead hidden within the physical form. I then understood that

A Mystery Unfolds

what we call virtue is simply our apprehension, but not necessarily our understanding, of the presence of the divine in a given life-form.

Thus, in the civic virtues Courage refers not only to our resolve to stand by our convictions, even at the risk of sacrificing our life, but also to our ability to control and educate the part of our soul that is subject to anger. It requires understanding, patience and non-attachment as we learn to walk away from the mindless passions of the herd and establish our own values. This requires time because such qualities grow out of experience. Justice consists in understanding the nature and value of duty and in ordering our life so that we may live in harmony with our fellows. Temperance means controlling the appetitive nature, which at the beginning is driven by instinct and full of self-interest. Temperance teaches us to harmonise appetite and reason that we may transcend the animal nature and become fit for greater things. Prudence is the manifestation of the rational part of the soul, which functions at its best when it is not serving the needs and demands of the animal nature. Thus, Prudence requires that we learn to manage our existence according to reason governed by a spiritual philosophy, because without such a philosophy we will never be free of the mundane world."

"But then", Ann replied, "I know what you are saying makes sense but it seems to me that virtue must be seen in conjunction with vice; I mean they have always been paired off, have they not? And it seems to me that vice is more prevalent in our world than virtue; a situation that seems to have existed forever. Indeed, the whole basis of civilisation rests on finding a means of living in harmony with each other for the greater good of the whole, is this not so; otherwise what is civilisation? So, if virtue is an expression of the divine in human form, what is vice?" Marcus responded slowly, his voice hesitant."It is difficult to understand vice without comprehending what is meant be the term evil, but what is 'evil'? In my experience there is no single universally accepted answer; though, as a rule of thumb most people identify evil as anything which threatens the existence and well being of human life and culture; which is as good a working model as any. Not so long ago we looked upon predators such as the wolf or the shark as evil creatures with our doom as their primary objective; other creatures such as the scorpion, the crocodile and the snake are still tarred with the same brush. But the truth of the matter is that these creatures simply behave according to their own nature, and more often than not they are more afraid of us than we are of them. Indeed, they are usually quite predictable; whereas human behaviour is not. We readily identify war and the acts of oppression by administrations such as the Nazis, Stalinists etc. as being typically evil; and it is usual to label murderers, rapists, pederasts, and drug dealers etc. as being evil as well. Perhaps this is because the abuse and destruction of human life seems to lie at the heart of the issue. Such views are certainly accepted as valid definitions of evil, but interestingly in some instances they may also be the cause of actions that an impartial observer might view as being equally evil; I'm thinking of a revenge killing by a mob for example. On the other hand, the anti-abortion lobby that seeks the protection of unborn children is also considered by many to be evil, so our definitions are not so clear cut as we might think.

A Mystery Unfolds

The term 'evil' has a dimension to it that more often than not baffles the reasoning of the secular mind. This dimension involves religion and religious issues, a dimension which over the last century has generally been dismissed by the secular world as archaic and irrational. So much so that many people no longer accept 'evil' in the moral sense, preferring instead to think of it as a psychological manifestation of a curable biological malfunction. In short, the nature and dynamics of evil has to all intents and purposes become a specialised branch of clinical psychology, and in many instances rightly so. However, even though the biological factors influencing behaviour are very important there is more to this subject than biochemical influences upon human psychology. From our perspective, the recognition and acceptance of the spiritual dimension of human existence is fundamental to a balanced understanding of this subject.

Where then do we go from here? Well, the scriptures inform us that the human soul is created in God's image, an image that is the ideal humanity is seeking to express. It is the divine potential that lies at the heart of human nature, and the evolutionary imperative 'to be' or 'to become' is the mechanism by which the unfolding of that divine potential will reach its fullest expression. I was taught that its nature is divine and consequently 'good', whilst evil is that which endeavours to manipulate the natural course of events in the evolutionary process for motives that have the perversion of that ideal at heart. I was further taught that good and evil are neither twins, nor opposites, they do not constitute a dualism describing two fundamental principles of existence engaged in eternal conflict, as some have maintained. This concept of good and evil (dualism) is an ancient argument formed by our limited intellects to describe our imperfect understanding of reality. Evil is not a separate thing, and it is important that we recognise this fact otherwise we concede to it the attribute of reality - a fundamental error with far reaching implications. Nevertheless, evil does exist, make no mistake about that, but it exists in the same way that a lie is the distortion or perversion of truth; it is the distortion or perversion of the good, just as Lucifer – originally an expression of goodness – was corrupted by a perverse view of his own self-worth.

Truth and Goodness are synonymous, truth defines that which is true, and that which is true stands in its own light, self-existent – it is reality, whereas a lie cannot exist of itself; it is always relative. Thus, evil is always a perversion or distortion of that which is good. This is epitomised in the person of Lucifer himself, otherwise known as Satan, the father of lies and the perpetrator of all things evil. He is a fallen angel; he was not created as the antithesis to the Good, nor was he created as an alternative or counterpoint to what we understand the angels to represent. It was through pride that he became the perversion of what his true nature represents. Thus, his actions – perversions of all that is true, natural and good, stem from within him, not from without; and so it is with human nature, although we may suffer the afflictions of evil from without, via the hands of those who have succumbed to evil, it is only through surrendering our own will that we lose ourselves in the perversion of our own nature."

Marcus hesitated for a moment. It was the first time I saw him give the impression of being unsure; he looked around as if he was

A Mystery Unfolds

looking for some kind of reassurance, then, seemingly resolving whatever dilemma that was bothering him, continued; "The information I am about to share with you is information that is generally given only to members of the Order, and I must warn you that it is no more than a rough guide, a working model. It is not to be taken as definitive, nor is it to be thought of as scientific, it is simply a working model that has been found useful to Order members in their work." Everyone immediately became very attentive to Marcus' words, wondering what great secrets he was about to reveal. Marcus continued, "The great ocean of life in which we all have our existence and from which we all draw and to which we all contribute is the group mind of life, known in certain schools as the World-Soul. We share this vast ocean of life with an infinity of other creatures, both visible and invisible. With some we interact, such as mammals, birds, fish and reptiles. Other creatures lie at the edges of our perception such as bacteria, viruses, amoebas etc., but, of the majority of creatures existing in the World-Soul we have no knowledge whatsoever. Every species has its own group mind, thus, our experience takes place within the group mind of humanity. Within its parameters we establish our basic identity as creatures, and within the context of the group mind of race and country we establish our identity as people. It is through the immediate cultural influences of our family and community that we establish our personality.

One of the most significant mechanisms in this process involves our response to the positive and negative aspects of our nature. On the one hand we are conscious of an aspect of our personality that is positive, creative, tolerant, caring and selfless, and on the other we are conscious of a side that is negative, destructive, intolerant, uncaring and selfish. Indeed, there are thoughts and inclinations that arise in our minds we would never wish to share with others because they are often embarrassing, repulsive or distasteful, and it comes as both a shock and a relief when we eventually discover that this experience is not unique to our individual selves, but in varying degrees is something we all share in common.

Individuals tend to personify unique characteristics. For example, some are noted for their generosity and selflessness whilst others are noted for their meanness or selfishness. Some are very sensitive to the needs of others whilst some couldn't care less about anyone or anything so long as their own needs are satisfied. Alas, most people are not simple creatures, but display complex combinations of positive and negative behaviour. These complex behaviours contribute to the individual's 'uniqueness' as a personality. Now what applies to the individual also applies to the family group, and by extension to the community.

Families demonstrate unique characteristics, personalities if you will, based upon the combined natures of family members; however, the personality of each family member is also shaped by the group dynamics of the family. This includes both positive and negative aspects of behaviour. The behaviour of young members of a family is strongly influenced by the behaviour of the elders, be they older siblings, parents or relatives. Thus the etiquette and behaviour patterns of the family shape individual personalities, who in turn shape the etiquette and behaviour patterns of the family; therefore, not only does a family have both a positive and negative nature, but also every member of the family contributes to that nature through their individual behaviour. The same principle applies to the community, be it large or small. Whether it is a traditional village, a district, a town or a city, a community embodies the most dominant characteristics of the family groups that live and operate within it. The community both shapes and is shaped by the behaviour of its members. This is also true of regions, states and countries, wherein the personality or the egregore of the group mind influences individuals in ways undreamt of by the majority of the population.

Group minds are conglomerates of social interaction – family, community, town/city, region, state, nation, race and humanity itself. Within the group mind of humanity exist sub groups consisting of the races, nations, religions, languages, political affiliations etc. These subgroups have evolving personalities known as egregores. Most of us belong to several group minds at the same time, and every one of us contributes to the nature and form of the faculties of the group minds to which they belong, which in turn influences and shapes the individual." Thus far I had been keeping up with Marcus. This was fascinating stuff, but that word, 'egregore', I couldn't help asking him, "What is an egregore?"

"The word 'egregore' is an uncommon word most frequently used today by occultists to signify entities that are magically created by an esoteric group or to signify the thought form of their group-mind; but in principle any community of like-minded people that joins together for a common purpose will in due course develop an egregore. The etymology of the word is unclear, but for the purpose of this discussion I am using the term to signify the personality of a Group Mind; it is to a group what the personality is to the individual. An egregore generally reflects the nature and level of understanding of its group in the context of society, and the egregore of humanity reflects the level of evolution of the group mind of humanity in its relationship to the divine archetype – the Logos. Egregores are little understood and greatly underestimated.

Another important factor is the way in which egregores influence human life. Compared with the life span of a nation or a civilisation, the life span of the average person is short, and on the face of it makes little impact upon the group mind, although there are some notable exceptions in every culture. Yet, even though the individual has little noticeable effect upon the group mind, every thought feeling and action generated by an individual contributes to the nature, quality and mass of the group mind. Thus all of humanity is contributing not only to the group mind as a whole but also to both a creative egregore and a destructive egregore within the group-mind – on any scale. This means that if all members of a family were to become destructive then the family would be destructive; and if all the families in a community were to become destructive then the community would become destructive, ad infinitum etc. The implications are profound indeed. The greater the scale the more defined the forms. Thus at a family level one may perceive in a vague sort of way certain creative or destructive characteristics that are typical of that family, but on a national or perhaps racial level these creative and destructive forces are expressed in forms that are easily recognised by the population,

A Mystery Unfolds

either individually or en masse. Furthermore, although the individual generally has little obvious effect upon the group mind, the egregores and archetypes within the group mind, both in their form and their nature, have an immense impact on the life of the individual, although generally the individual is not consciously aware of it.

All cultures have a classical representation of both goodness and evil, thus in the Christian world the classical embodiment of goodness, the ideal, is defined in the form and nature of Jesus Christ and the classical embodiment of evil – the antithesis of the ideal – is expressed in the form and nature of Satan. In Christian terms Jesus Christ is acknowledged as the perfect model for humanity – the exemplar of the divine ideal embodied in human form. Alternatively, Satan is portrayed as the antithesis or perversion of the ideal, frequently described either as a cold-blooded reptile, the archetypal enemy of humanity, or a depraved animal such as a wolf-like or bullish creature, bent on satisfying its bestial appetites above all else. Our ancestors understood this and in their cosmology placed the soul of humanity between a realm governed by goodness (heaven) and a realm ruled by evil (hell). That Heaven and Hell exist is unquestionable, that they exist in physical terms is debatable, but their existence in metaphysical terms is irrefutable. However, the term metaphysical does not simply apply to a refined intellectual construct but to a spiritual reality that is the eternal substrate of the material world of the senses. In this reality the apparent polarity of creative and destructive forces is better understood not as opposites but in the context of Thesis ~ Antithesis. This state of affairs is reflected in the group mind of humanity and all of us are influenced by it from the day we are born if not earlier. In the context of this cosmology the soul aspires to the good, for in doing so it aligns itself with and realises the ideal, whereas surrendering to the instinctive and bestial instincts, aligns the soul with the antithesis of the ideal which ultimately leads to the negation of being; thus, all souls are beset by powerful forces operating within the group mind.

If virtue is the end goal, it is because virtue is a manifestation of divinity and the purpose of the faculties of the soul is the expression of the divine, whereas vice is the corruption and perversion of them. In developing our nature, in cultivating and refining it so that it may serve the highest purpose we can envisage, we grow in spirit and slowly shed the influences of the "garments" that we have worn throughout our lives. In Kabbalistic terms the student who has mastered the Nephesh and cared for it with kindness, is given entrance to the house of the Ruach, whose powers transform the civic virtues into a powerhouse of Catharsis. Within the illuminating presence of the Ruach the student begins a new life, a life that is no longer rooted in the darkness of complete ignorance, but a life that increases in knowledge as it grows in the 'Presence' of the Divine. In this blessed state the soul 'comes of age'." Marcus fell silent, and by silent consensus we all took a break. I went outside for a few minutes to clear my head and take in a breath of air. What the old monk had just said was quite mind-blowing; I mean, growing in the 'Presence of the Divine' as opposed to being tossed to and fro by the forces of human nature is an amazing concept. I stood looking up at the stars, barely

A Mystery Unfolds

comprehending the sense of infinity they implied. In a state of awe I tried to feel the Presence of God but all I could feel was how small and insignificant I was in relation to the vastness of the night sky. I stood for a while, completely silent, tears running down my face. I felt so indescribably alone and wretched in the immensity of the cosmos that all I wanted to do was run away and hide. With this in mind I turned to leave but found my way barred by the figure of Marcus. He handed me a tissue and put his hand on my shoulder; the warmth from his hand flowed through every fibre of my being spreading a peace beyond description. He said, very quietly, "Be still my son; it is ever the way for those who are called. Now, come, let us rejoin the others." With this he turned and led me back into the meeting. I composed myself and went in search of a cup of coffee for both Marcus and myself. When I returned he was in conversation with Leo, Ruth and Louise. Ruth was in the middle of telling him that we had spent some time in the Library researching the Rose Priory; "….and it seems that there has been a religious house on this site for more than a thousand years, but what we were really looking for was evidence that there really is a complex warren of tunnels and caves beneath this site." Marcus smiled, put his finger to his lips to signal that we should now be silent. He then said, "If you want to see the tunnels beneath the Priory come back tomorrow morning, about six o'clock." I couldn't believe my ears; without putting up any resistance Marcus had committed himself to showing us the labyrinth beneath the Priory. Well, the evening passed in a blur. I don't remember anything that was discussed. All I remember was going home and getting up very early to come back to the Priory for six o'clock.

Part Seven

The Heart Of The Matter

We met just before six at the Priory, every one of us looking bleary-eyed. Marcus, on the other hand was standing at the door looking as fresh as ever; he led us into the kitchen where fresh coffee, croissant and toast were just being placed on the table by one of the Brothers. Freshly boiled eggs lay steaming in a basket amidst jars of various jams and marmalades. The monk, speaking in a German, or perhaps Scandinavian accent, said with a grin; "Good morning to you all, I'm brother Luke and it's a pleasure to meet you all. You will be gone for a little while, so we thought it wise to give you breakfast first. The Prior thought you might have missed yours having got up so early." We tucked in with unabashed enthusiasm; Brother Luke was absolutely right, none of us had thought to eat before leaving so we were all pretty hungry. Marcus sat, coffee in hand, said quietly, "You know your interest in this place has been noticed; it's refreshing to see such enthusiasm." Leo replied. "We thought you would do everything in your power to stop us exploring the subterranean levels of the Priory." "Normally that would certainly be the case, you see some of the tunnels aren't safe, so we generally dismiss their existence as an exaggeration or an old folk tale. Occasionally, we show a few people around, but not often. However, your enthusiasm and interest in the spiritual work has convinced me otherwise. Just remember, few people have seen what you are about to see; I hope you will be able to cope with it."

We finished breakfast and followed Marcus through what looked like a pantry door. It led into a long narrow store-room, with well stocked shelves running along each side, at the end of which a flight of stairs led down into a cellar. In the cellar Marcus unlocked a small solid wooden door. Stone steps spiralled downward. We followed him, stepping into a cool inky darkness. For several minutes we descended in the dark, the only sound being made by our feet clattering on the stone steps. I tried to keep count but after a hundred steps or so I gave up. Eventually we reached the bottom, where we huddled together feeling simultaneously excited and unsure of ourselves. Curiously, it wasn't dark here; a soft light illuminated a long passageway that seemed wide enough to drive a small car along it. I looked about me, there was no obvious source to account for the light; it seemed as if it emanated directly from the walls themselves. As my eyes became accustomed to the light I noticed that there were several tunnels branching off from this one, which seemed to be the main artery. I looked at Marcus and babbled; "It's true then, there are tunnels and caves under the Priory." "Yes", he replied, "of course there are!"

Louise said, "When we were in the Central Library we learned that in medieval times the brothers of the Order used to sleep down here; is that really true?" "To a limited extent" replied Marcus, "You will discover that it is extremely quiet and peaceful down here; ideal for developing skills in meditation and contemplation. From that point of view spending prolonged periods of time down here is extremely beneficial; it also has the added benefit of being extremely private." Leo, looking absolutely fascinated by all of this, said excitedly; "What about the legend of the fabulous library, is there any truth in that legend; does it actually exist?" "Oh yes, but not quite as you would expect. Come with me and I shall show you a part of it."

We followed Marcus along the main gallery, as he called it; it went on a long way. The same soft light illuminated everything equally, without any variation. I asked Marcus about it, but all he said was that one day I would understand, but not today. As we walked I noticed that there were strange markings at the point where tunnels branched off from the main gallery. They were not in any language I knew, but looked something like the sigils found in ancient alchemical manuscripts. I thought to myself that I must ask him about them, but for now I remained silent. At some point we turned into a side-tunnel on the right. We walked on for a minute or so and stopped. Before us stood a solid wooden door; Marcus turned and said to us; "Before we go in I must inform you that according to Order teachings it is accepted that it is possible to convey information in many ways. A book of words is only one means, and not necessarily the most ideal. Behind this door you will find information conveyed in a different way than the written word. It is as a matter of fact a great library, but not as you would expect it." With that he turned the handle and gently pushed the door. I half expected it to creak open like an old castle door in a 'B' movie, but it pivoted silently, perfectly balanced on its hinges.

The Rose Priory Dialogues

We entered into a room that was completely dark, except for the light that fell through the open door. Within, I could see nothing at all, not even the walls or the ceiling. We entered, and before we knew it the door had silently closed behind us. The room was now completely dark, not a glimmer of light found its way herein. I couldn't even feel the presence of my companions, all that I was aware of was an incredible feeling of being alone, so great was it that an intense fear welled up inside me. Surprisingly my reaction was not to cry out to my companions, but to pour out my soul in silent fervent prayer to everything I held to be sacred for guidance and illumination. How long I stood in that state I know not, but at some point I opened my eyes and lifted my head and saw that my head was encircled by a golden light,a light that filled my soul with peace. I also noticed that whilst my head was encircled with light my feet, and my lower body, remained in complete darkness, and I intuitively understood that the Soul is a reflection of the Unity suspended between the Light and Darkness, the head representing Gnosis and Unity whilst the body represents instinct and diversity. I knew then that my vision was not of the senses and the realisation dawned on me that it was not by intellectual striving that we grow in understanding, but through prayer and meditation.

I looked around me and saw that my companions were arrayed as I was. Marcus stood apart, his whole being enveloped in light. He beckoned silently with his hand, indicating that we should follow him. He touched the wall and a door opened; we followed him through the door into another chamber. Inside I perceived a noble Woman cloaked, indeed veiled in every hue of

The Heart Of The Matter

indigo and blue; a silvery white light gently radiated from the centre of her bosom. Upon her head was a crown with the crescent moon resting upon it. On her lap lay a great book closed. Her presence was so great that I fell to my knees and out of my mouth fell the words; "Teach me noble lady, teach me that I may learn," Silently she communicated; "I am the Recipient – the Passive; I am that which complements what you have experienced in the first chamber. I am the Link between Unity and the Soul. I am the Holy Sanctuary. I hold the Book of Knowledge which may be read only by those souls who have the power to lift my veil." As I gazed upon her my vision became as one thing and as I gazed I saw her veil gradually become fainter and fainter, and for a fleeting moment I beheld the beauty of her face – then she vanished from my sight.

Before I had time to gather my thoughts Marcus took hold of my arm and led me into the next chamber. I was led through a curtain made of an ethereal stuff woven into the most beautiful fabric imaginable. Herein I beheld a beautiful Imperial Woman clothed in Majesty, and wearing a crown of authority. To one side of her stood an enormous golden eagle, larger than any bird seen on Earth; above her was a canopy, formed, so it seemed, from the wings of angels. I knelt before her, as every soul must before the Queen of Heaven. she spoke to me in the gentlest voice imaginable: "I am the termination of the First and Second; in me the equilibrium is complete. I am the Law of the World; with my sceptre do I govern it. With one hand I draw down the Spirit and with the other I raise up its Negation, and in my womb is Man conceived." Her beauty was so great that I was overwhelmed by it and I could gaze upon her no longer. I closed my eyes only for a moment and found myself, with my companions standing outside her chamber; it was obvious that they must have had a similar experience to my own. I also noticed each of them was enveloped in light and I wondered if it were true of myself; I looked down at myself, but it was impossible for me to tell. None of us could, or indeed wanted to speak, we simply stood in silence lost in our own personal reverie.

Marcus spoke to us, drawing us out of ourselves; then he led us to a steep flight of steps. As we climbed, somewhere in the back of my mind I pondered on the fact that we were actually ascending, and I was curious about that, but the reason why evaded me. When we reached the top of the stairs we stepped onto a landing where a large wooden door stood before us. Marcus said to us all, "Before you is the fourth chamber, and there are many other chambers beyond it. You may enter or you may retire to go back to your life without shame or regret; but know that such an opportunity as this arises very rarely and never twice in the same life-time; so think hard before you decide." In silence we all looked at each other; In my mind giving up was not an option, whatever the consequences. Both Louise and Ruth smiled and shrugged their shoulders, nodding towards the door that led into the fourth chamber. Leo pointed towards the door and we all moved towards it. Marcus turned the handle and the door glided open, we entered into what was evidently a throne room. I beheld a King sitting upon his throne, and before the sovereign majesty of his face I bent my knee and my head. I felt his gaze upon my head, his searching eyes entered my heart and my mind, and I heard him say: "I am not the

The Heart Of The Matter

Absolute, however, for humanity I am the realisation of the Absolute: I am the Will of the Unity; my Sceptre is the sign of Power; with it I rule mankind, for my Law shall be mankind's Law; to me all souls must turn, for all that relates to the World in which they move is accountable to that Law." The king fell silent and his gaze passed from my heart; I felt Marcus' hand upon my arm and I followed him. I know we left by another door, but I remember nothing of it. We entered into another chamber, the fifth I think. Here I beheld a venerable man seated upon a throne. I saw that upon his head was not a crown of a king, but a mystic sign, and he was arrayed in the white robes of sanctity. His was the presence of grace rather than the power of authority. He spoke these words to me; "Kneel and worship, but worship neither king nor prince, nor what you see before you, but only the Lord God. Know this, although I am enthroned I am not a king of this world; my sceptre is the sign of spiritual authority; with it I rule the souls of mankind. I am the Voice of the Law of the Spirit. I am the bond of reunion between the soul created and the breath from which its creation proceeded." He then fell silent and with awe in my heart I withdrew, following Marcus, my guide. He led me to another chamber.

Herein I found myself in darkness. I stood still, seeking an inner light within my soul. Gradually, a dim light descended from the apex of the chamber, it grew both in brightness and intensity, and when I found the courage to look at it I beheld in astonishment the most beautiful Eye of a Spiritual being looking down upon me. Silently, in the depths of my soul I felt the words emerge, "Behold, the Eye of the World! Through it the mind realises the beauty of the manifestation of the Unity; through it love reaches the soul, bringing Man and Woman to the completion of their destiny. Learn and understand the mystery of this sign. This is the point from which two roads diverge; along the one descends the Spirit of Light; along the other descends the Spirit of Darkness." The vision slowly faded from my sight and I stood, head bowed, meditating upon its significance. I remembered the words of the Lord; "The light of the body is the eye: if therefore thine eye be single, thy whole body shall be full of light." With those words engraved in my heart I followed Marcus out of the chamber.

We followed Marcus up another steep flight of steps. Marcus informed us that we had reached the seventh chamber, and again offered us the opportunity to turn back with our dignity intact. In silence we declined, preferring to press on regardless. We entered the seventh chamber and I found myself standing in the midst of an ancient landscape. I saw nothing for a while; but then, I heard the whiz of an arrow, and beheld a great stag struck down by it. Looking around I saw the majestic figure of a man, radiant, like a conqueror, holding in his extended hand the bow from which the arrow had been discharged. He called to me; "What do you see?" I replied, "I see the weak overcome by the strong." He then said, "Behold, I am the Man Conqueror; Man the emblem of the Creator. I am more than Nature, I am Nature illuminated by the Spirit of the Eternal, and therefore do I overcome Nature." I left this chamber somewhat perplexed by what I had seen. I passed immediately into the next chamber where I beheld a sword standing unsupported on the point of its hilt, and in surprise exclaimed; "What does this sign mean?" Marcus said; "Between

The Heart Of The Matter

the soul and Nature a permanent struggle exists; what the soul attains by labour it loses again if the labour should cease. This is the sign of Equilibrium, the balance between opposing forces, between Good and Evil in the created world. This is the sign of the Spirit of Justice, which with the power of the sword separates opposing combatants. I stood gazing at this symbol for some considerable time; I felt bewildered by it. Beckoned by Marcus I left with some reluctance. I proceeded to the next chamber praying for guidance and understanding, because I was now realising that any understanding I had stood for little in this world.

I followed Marcus into this ninth chamber and found myself looking into the eyes of an old monastic, whose countenance was serene and radiant; for him age seemed to have no afflictions and wisdom shone forth from his eyes. In his right hand he held aloft a burning lamp, and in his left hand he held a stout wooden staff. I greeted him reverently in the name of the Lord and he addressed me thus: "When I was young I took the Path of Light, and my reward has been great. Wisdom shines in the lamp which illuminates my path. Around my soul I have drawn the Mantle of Protection which shall ward off Evil. My staff is the Staff of Strength I have acquired on my path, and on it I lean with security in my ascent towards Truth." The peace and serenity of this old sage filled my soul with elation, and the glow of divine love emanating from him seemed to penetrate into me like a precious gift from his presence. In all that I had witnessed so far I had tried to keep in mind the teachings that we had received from Marcus, particularly with regard to symbolism and allegory. Yet, even though his teachings were true and had stood me in good stead I still felt inadequately prepared for this situation; not that I had been forewarned, but I was struggling with it nonetheless.

I met with my companions outside the old sage's chamber. They looked just as I felt; it was obvious none of us were having an easy time of it. The nature of the forces that we were each experiencing, and who is to say that our experiences were comparable, were far beyond the commonplace of our human experience. Meekly, we followed Marcus to the next floor where the tenth chamber lay. As we climbed the steps I again mused upon the fact that we were ascending, at this point the evasive thought emerged 'but we were underground', or were we? Before I could answer that question to myself we entered the tenth chamber. Herein I beheld a circle turning upon an invisible axis. I looked upon it turning effortlessly, indeed, I was transfixed; it was so enchanting. Marcus said to me; "Behold, the symbol of Eternity, the symbol of the incessant action of Time. The Circle is ever moving; it ascends and descends; so ascends the Spirit of God to the summit, so descends the Spirit of Evil to the abyss; yet the Circle is unbroken; so from the Good the descent to Evil is possible, so from Evil the ascent to Good is possible. This is the Chamber of Equilibrium. Below is the seventh chamber, wherein you beheld the Conqueror – the holder of Power, the symbol of Creative Force. In the chamber above you will see the Symbol of Destruction. Here you see the ascent and descent of a circle that is one and unbroken; Yet know that a greater Circle exists which the human eye cannot see; turning without ceasing throughout Eternity. The Spirit of Creation creates and the Spirit of Destruction destroys; and the circle is the equilibrium without which there would be no manifestation of Unity, and if there were no Manifestation of the Unity there would be no manifestation of life." Marcus stopped speaking and I stood for a long time contemplating the moving circle.

Eventually he took my arm and led me to the next chamber, wherein I saw a Virgin goddess standing before me, radiant in all the splendour of youth and strength. Beneath her feet a dragon lay motionless, as if it were dead, and clasped in her hand were ears of ripened corn. With a voice which had the ring of silver without tremor and without fear she addressed me thus; "Within me lies hid the germ of vitality. To you my hand may seem weak, but true strength lies not in the flesh but in the Spirit, and because my heart is pure, I know no fear, and with my foot I curb the dragon beneath me." It was so lovely a vision it made my heart leap with joy; slowly it faded from my sight and I pensively followed Marcus to the twelfth chamber, my mind filled with the beauty of the virgin who had appeared to me. In the twelfth chamber I found myself again in complete darkness, and as I gazed apprehensively into its depths a sign materialised slowly, revealing the form of a cross. Marcus said; "Behold the sign of the Revealed law; out of the darkness it proceeds, and the soul must bow to it." As I gazed upon it more intently, the face of a man seemed to appear to me enclosed by a triangle hanging downwards at the base of the cross." A voice within me cried out; "What does this signify?" Marcus replied; "Woe unto the soul who filled with pride presumes to rebel against the Revealed Law, for destruction awaits such a soul. Vain are they who seek to rebel against that which the Eternal has revealed, by submission will the soul rise, by rebellion the soul's face is turned from the Light and its progress delayed." I saw within me a previous event where Marcus laboured to point out to any who would listen that we must rise above the influences of the instinctive nature if we are to grow in the spirit, and recognised in an instant Nietzsche's folly in presuming a material superman could ever be the centre of Creation.

Wearily we climbed to another floor, the fifth I believe, I was beginning to think that this journey would never end; my legs ached and my head hurt. Nevertheless, perseverance was the watchword, so girding my loins, as it were, we entered another chamber – the thirteenth. I beheld before me a luxuriant meadow; it was a vision of Eden itself, filled with a variety of splendid flora and luxuriant flowers nodding to each other in their joy of existence. As I enjoyed this exquisite vision a wintry breath approached, its icy blast chilling my soul, and I saw the vision of Death looming before me. In one hand he held a great scythe and in the other an empty basket; and he mowed down the flowers and threw them into the basket; and it seemed to me that they turned into dead men's heads; and some wore crowns and others the humble hood of the hermit; and some had the golden hair of youth, and others the whitened locks of old age. Again the inner voice of my soul cried out; "O Terror of the world, what are you?" Marcus spoke; "He is the link between the known and the unknown. That which appears to be gold in the world he will turn into base metal, and that which appears to be base metal he will turn into gold. As the ocean dissolves and absorbs the Salt of the World, so does he, for he is the solvent of humanity, and out of that which is he makes that which will be." Marcus stopped speaking and the vision of

The Heart Of The Matter

Death departed from me, and I saw once more the green meadow filled with flowers. The Marcus spoke again; "The Spirit of Life is the antagonist of the Spirit of Stagnation, for stagnation is the negation of life. In the Unity nothing is created, nothing is destroyed. To the sage, therefore, Death has no terrors, for the sage knows that without death there could be no life, without darkness no light, without negation no manifestation of Reality. Death is the key which opens unto the soul a further stage on the Path of the manifestation of the Unity.

From this chamber Marcus led us into another wherein I beheld an angel who poured the Waters of Life out of a pitcher into a receptacle far below. Marcus said to me; "In the world wherein you live the mind perceives the existence of individuality, which is caused by the Waters of Life descending in varying degrees into matter, its opposite. Now the angel, when fertilising the world by pouring upon it the Waters of Life, gives the soul the conception of Justice, which is to be the light by which the soul is guided on its path through the material world. The angel is therefore the emblem of Temperance, which is the principle that should govern individual creatures in the world. Before I could compose my thoughts Marcus led me out of this chamber into the next. Herein I found myself again in complete darkness, but this time I was full of foreboding. As I stood in the darkness, out of its depths emerged a great beast emanating evil, a dragon biting its tail. Seized with fear I reached out to my guide who said, "Calm yourself and know that this is the Circle of Evil. Woe to the soul that steps into the shadow of the light, for the gloom shall grow greater and greater, and against the fatal power of the dragon's ring the soul will struggle in vain. Who falls into the magic Circle no regrets can avail, for an eternity seems to separate such a soul from the Path of Reunion." Marcus then led me out of that fearful chamber; indeed, I was so anxious to be free of it I almost ran through the doorway.

In my haste I collided with my companions who were anxiously waiting outside. They too looked terribly shaken. Marcus asked us once more if we wanted to call it a day. I must say that I was sorely tempted, but something within me demanded that I persist in this venture. I half expected the others to give up and go home but they didn't; they stood their ground, probably driven by the same force that was driving me onward. Whatever it was, we ascended the steep flight of steps with an urgency that said more about escaping what lay behind than what lay ahead. We entered a vast room, vaster than any cathedral; herein stood a massive tower of great strength. I perceived the master of this tower with his attendants enjoying their security behind the battlements of their stronghold. It appeared so strong and secure that it looked as if it would not perish but last until the end of the world. As I gazed at it I heard a great roar and I beheld a mighty thunderbolt descending from a cloud; it struck the tower and the battlements parted asunder; the master with his attendants were hurled from the heights of the tower to the ground. I looked on in amazement; one moment there stood a great tower standing firm even to eternity, the next moment it was utterly destroyed. I asked Marcus what it meant. He replied, "Behold the Sign of the Fall! The soul is a spiritual being that has entered the world and put on the burden of the material body. Behold the Symbol of the Spirit of the Unity, which to your eyes is invisible, incarnated in the world which lies open to your senses."

When this vision passed away I followed Marcus, greatly puzzled by the vision and his words. He led me into the next chamber, and as I entered I felt the breath of Spring upon me, and my heart, which had been sorely vexed by the falling tower, leapt for joy; and as I looked I beheld the vision of a lovely maiden; her golden tresses were crowned with a diadem of seven stars; she sat in the middle of a green meadow enamelled, as it were, with the glory of flowers, and by her side was a fountain from which poured forth the pure Water of the Earth. As I gazed upon her loveliness she opened her lips and spoke, and my soul was so moved that tears flowed from my eyes for the joy of the softness of her voice, which was like the music of a harp in the stillness of the night. And she said: " In the depth of the material world lies hidden the Water which wells up in the Fountain of Immortality. I am the eternal youth of Nature; the glory of the Sun I have absorbed into my golden tresses; from my diadem of stars do I draw down the Spirit into the physical body; into the fallen soul I breathe the hope of Redemption; through me comes to the soul the courage to struggle against the bondage in which it is placed."

I stood for a long time contemplating this vision, it was so beautiful and yet so profound. Indeed, if Marcus had not drawn me away I could still be there. With some regret I was led out of that extraordinary room into the last on this floor. Here again I found myself in utter darkness, but this time the sense of foreboding was not present, instead I was filled with despondency as I beheld the world spread out before me illuminated by the pale and sickly light of the moon; under this baleful orb men were struggling against men; wild beasts were struggling against wild beasts; and the reptiles of the Earth came out of their hiding places to gather their spoil. In my sorrow I asked Marcus to explain this vision; "This is the last term; it is the ultimate descent of the spirit of the Unity into the depths of the Abyss of Negation. This is the realm of Chaos in the world, it is the rule of the passions let loose. This is the triumph of matter, matter absorbing Spirit and on the verge of throttling it." The sight of this vision filled me with so great a terror that I felt as if a great mountain of stone was being piled upon my soul to crush it, so much so that beneath the strain of it my mind gave way and I fell into a faint.

When I recovered the use of my senses the vision had gone. I composed myself and Marcus led me quietly out of this chamber of despair. My companion and I started to move towards the stairs that led to the next floor but Marcus stopped us, saying, "Before we go on let us pause for a moment and reflect on what you have accomplished thus far. You have ascended six floors of a tower." We all looked totally surprised at this statement, 'what tower?' was the first question that popped into my mind, and I could see the same question in the eyes of my companions, "and you have visited three chambers on each floor, eighteen chambers in all. Now understand the meaning of what you have seen. In the first six chambers you were introduced to principles of the Universe; in the next six you were introduced to a world of Law and gained thereby knowledge of the Spirit of Preservation; in the last six you have been introduced to a world of verities, of unassailable facts. The sum of them all alluding to the Breath of Unity descending into the world of Darkness. What you shall see in the remaining chambers alludes to the yearning for Reunion, to the Spirit of the Eternal proceeding back into the Unity whence it came forth."

When he had spoken thus, Marcus led the way up a long staircase, narrow and steep at the beginning but broadening out as we advanced. When we reached the top we entered the nineteenth chamber. At first I saw nothing at all; the room was filled with a shapeless mist permeated by a vivifying luminosity. Gradually, in the depth of the mist I saw a point of condensation; gradually it assumed a more definite shape, and then it appeared to me like a pure crystal of salt suspended in the ocean. Slowly the crystal vanished, and through the spot where it had been I saw hills forming; then they became more distinct and I saw the shapes of trees appearing, and flowers of every hue, with butterflies and insects buzzing among them, and the fishes were leaping in the rivers; and as I marvelled at this sight a glorious light broke through the mist, and I saw beneath me a lovely garden in which children, youths and maidens, played among the flowers, rejoicing in the gift of life. Then I heard Marcus speak, "Behold, the Spirit of the Eternal through the chaos of the Material World has reached to the manifestation of Humanity."

Eventually, the mist closed around me again, and I followed Marcus to the next chamber, the twentieth. Herein I saw spread out before me the Field of Solitude – the burial place of Humanity, where no living thing stirred. As I gazed upon the waste of life therein I heard the voice of Israel calling to Humanity. And I saw in the centre of the field of Solitude Azrael – the angel of Death – sitting in meditation; and at the sound of the trumpet he rose and flapped his sabled pinions like a tired bird about to retire to his rest, then he drew his great wings around his form and was still, for the sleep of eternity was upon him. And in the Field of Solitude I saw the graves open and the dead rising from them, and the rending of their grave clothes was like the roar of the sea seeking to break down the barrier of the land. Marcus took hold of my trembling arm and said; "fear not, it is the voice of the Eternal calling to Humanity. Behold the Breath of Unity rising to the Spirit World and casting aside the shackles of the Material World!"

When the vision had faded away I followed Marcus to the last chamber on this floor of the tower. It was the twenty-first. Herein there appeared before me a young man riding on a fine horse, and with eyes burning with desire he gazed steadfastly at a young girl who danced before him glorious in her nakedness, and her hair was adorned with garlands of roses. By his side an old hag hobbled along, holding his stirrup with one hand, while she held an hourglass in the other, in which I saw the sands were fast running out. As I looked I saw of a sudden a deep precipice ahead, and at that moment a hideous dog rushed forth and bit the legs of the horse to urge him on his career. As the rider grew closer to the precipice, the young girl who danced before him changed in my sight, and the colour in her cheek changed into the waxen hue of Death, while the petals of the roses on her head shrivelled and fell to the ground, and I saw her hair spreading out across the sky like the grey threads of a spider's web. Then the young man, having no power to check the fury of his steed, passed away and was lost in the abyss, and my heart was sore and heavy with pity for this young man. Then, I heard Marcus say to me: "Watch and behold!"

The Heart Of The Matter

Again a young man appeared to me, and he was clad in armour, and in his hand was a great spear. Wild and dangerous beasts I saw leaping across his path, but he looked neither to the right nor to the left, but with the power of his spear drove them away. And I saw him begin the ascent of a steep mountain full of obstacles, but they seemed to give way before him, and as he reached the summit the sun shone forth illuminating his armour, and in the glory of that light the vision faded from my sight. Then Marcus said to me: "In the first chamber on this floor you saw the Divine Spirit rising though Matter to the human world. In the next chamber you saw the rise of the Divine Spirit from the human world to the Spiritual World. Now this is the meaning of what you have seen in this chamber. In the world in which you live an Equilibrium exists between Matter and the Divine Spirit. Now in the heart of every soul lies a point on which this Equilibrium is poised, and this point is the mystery of the soul's individuality. It has the power of turning the balance to the right or to the left, towards matter which leads to the Abyss, or towards the Divine Spirit, which accelerates the moment of reunion with the Unity. Woe unto any soul who lets the idleness of one hour impair the power of its individuality to turn the balance towards the Light."

Marcus then fell silent and led me from the chamber. I moved towards my companions and Marcus said: "There is one more chamber before you, but into that chamber you must go alone. The way is steep and difficult." He pointed the way to a flight of steps which led, so it seemed, to the highest pinnacle of the tower. Wearily we began the ascent, and when we had reached the summit I saw before me the entrance to the chamber closed by a heavy veil.

The Rose Priory Dialogues

I pushed it aside and entered . As the veil fell back behind me it felt as if a gravestone had fallen upon my grave, and that I was forever separated from the world of humanity. A deep sense of solitude crept over me and a great desire to pray, and kneeling down I worshipped the Unknown Godhead, the source and creator of all, seeking for Illumination, and slowly, by degrees, the knowledge of the things which I had seen in my ascent increased within me, and when I lifted up my eyes I saw that the chamber in which I stood was formed like an ellipse, and that in the centre a figure sat upon a throne, neither Man nor Woman, but humanity in the Womb of Time – the Ellipse of the Absolute. And as I gazed and marvelled, I saw a mystic flower at the summit of the Chamber open its four great petals, on each of which a Sign burnt in fire, and from the depths of the flower three rays of light shone upon the figure beneath, illuminating it with splendour, so that I saw the overpowering serenity of its face. As I contemplated this vision the figure crossed its hands, so that forefinger was extended against forefinger, and with the tips of the forefingers it touched its lips, placing thereon the Seal of Silence. The beauty of that face was so overwhelming that I covered my eyes with my hands, and when I opened them I found myself alongside my companions, standing in the familiar study where our weekly meetings take place.

We looked at each other in complete amazement. Louise was the first to speak; "What exactly happened, I mean, did we or did we not just ascend a mysterious tower, or was it just myself in those amazing rooms, because that's how it seemed to me. Except, I distinctly remember being with you all, but not in the rooms themselves, just outside." Leo and Ruth were of the same opinion.

The Heart Of The Matter

I didn't know what to say so I just kept quiet. It seemed as if I had experienced the most amazing dream imaginable, yet it wasn't a dream, how could it have been, we had all shared it together in the flesh. I wondered if we had been unwittingly subjected to group hypnosis or perhaps drugged during our breakfast, but I was unwilling to accept that Marcus would stoop to such low cunning. I asked the others what they thought had happened, they were of the same opinion, however, Leo speculated that our experiences could have been generated by suggestion whilst Louise and Ruth thought how it happened didn't really matter, that it happened was all that counted; otherwise we would have to be extremely suspicious of Marcus. It was a good point, because none of us could find the slightest reason for doubting his motives or his integrity. We agreed to ask him, if we could find him, about what had really took place in that tower; if indeed there actually was a tower.

As we conversed Marcus entered the room pushing a trolley laden with tea, coffee and sandwiches. He said; "We should eat something, it's been a long day." We all sat down around the fire and tucked into the food. I was far hungrier than I realised, I looked at my watch, and it was just after five in the afternoon. Leo said to Marcus, "We are all in agreement that we have shared a common experience, it was extraordinarily beautiful and profound, but how did it happen; was it real or was it an induced group hallucination? Please answer this riddle for us." Marcus replied; "Leo, did I not inform you that there is more than one way to convey information, and that words in books are not necessarily the best way. Well, your experience was real, it was not induced through hypnosis or drugs, as a matter of fact the answer is quite simple, but nonetheless fantastic." Ruth asked him if we actually went underground at all. Marcus laughed, "Of course you did, and you will probably go down to the library again, but not quite yet, not immediately anyway." I asked him how we got back here, into this room in such a spectacular fashion. Again he laughed; "One thing at a time, one thing at a time. You know, right now you are not really listening to me; you are simply trying to deal with the anomaly in your experience. I said earlier that there is more than one way to convey information, and you have had information conveyed to you by another means, albeit a means that is strange to you, but that does not mean that it is a trick or some kind of illusion. The facts are these, you descended to the cave system below; you walked along the main gallery; you entered the library, which is a cave system of its own; and you read what each room had to tell you. But you did not read with your eyes but with your mind. Each room has embedded within it thought-forms that a sensitive mind can tune into. The thought-forms you experienced were created many centuries ago and have been reinforced through constant use ever since. It is possible to engage with the same thought-forms repeatedly; however, the answers to the questions that arise in each engagement lie within your own soul. Do not make the mistake of assuming what you saw was anything other than thought-forms created for the edification of the soul – they are not astral doorways into alternative realities. How you returned here is another matter and not up for discussion, as yet."

Marcus then got to his feet and beckoned us to follow him. He led us into the garden and pointed up across the meadow towards the woodland. "What do you see?" We all looked, although I was puzzled by this turn of events. "Trees," I said, "Well done lad," he replied, "but look a little harder," "Oh!" said Ruth, "Is that a small tower hidden within the trees?" "Where?" exclaimed Leo, "Up there to the left" said Louise, "you can just see the top of it sticking over the trees." "Oh yes!" he said incredulously, I followed the line of Ruth's arm and surely enough I could just make out the outline of a tower, not so different from a Church tower without a spire; I could just see the battlements of the parapet. I exclaimed; "Well I never..., there really is a tower." Louise said, "Marcus, how old is it?" "Late Saxon, I think, but nobody really know for sure. Some of our own archives suggest it is much older, but we don't advertise its presence or its antiquity, for obvious reasons."

The evening was setting in and the air was turning cold so we returned to the study. We talked throughout the evening, mostly about our experiences, and what we should do about them. Marcus reminded us that when all was said and done they were thought-forms, albeit profound and beautiful thought-forms, but we should never forget that, "By names and by images are all things awakened and reawakened in the sphere of sensation." I asked Marcus if it were likely that any person entering the tower would have the same experiences. He said that it was theoretically possible but highly unlikely as the conditions had to be just right, and that the right conditions included the mind of the person involved. "Invariably a person would be guided through the library by someone like myself; alternatively, if any were to enter alone most would probably find themselves experiencing strange feelings or odd atmospheres, and would probably leave in a state of anxiety, and glad to be away from the place." Marcus concluded the day by saying; "You all have a great deal to think about. Remember what I said at the beginning, few people will ever experience what you have experienced today; how you cope with it is not just an academic question. You have been introduced to some important truths and concepts about universal realities, which will inevitably have an impact upon your lives. If you have need to talk to me then get in touch, at any time of the day or night." On that note we left the Priory.

Part Eight

Insight and Resolution

Early the following morning I received a telephone call from Leo. Like myself, neither he nor Louise had slept a wink; they hadn't even bothered going to bed. Leo wondered if we should all meet up and talk about our recent experiences at the Rose Priory, especially in the tower. It seemed like a good idea to me. I asked him if he had spoken with Ruth; he said he'd call her straight away and get back to me. Whilst Leo went off to talk with Ruth I took a long hot shower – hoping to wash the cobwebs out of my mind. I was showered and dressed and just making some coffee when Leo got back to me to say that he'd had a long chat with Ruth and they had agreed to meet in the Atlantis Café at eleven o'clock.

A few minutes after eleven we were all sitting around a table looking at each other, each wondering who would start, and what they might say. If the others were thinking as I was then we would all be wondering if it was ever possible to go back into the mundane world, to pick up where they left off before yesterday's experience. "I don't know what to say" muttered Leo, "nor me", said Louise and Ruth together; All I could say was; "I think we should go and see Marcus, he'll probably know what to say. What do you think?" "Oh! Well we could, but would he be there?" mumbled Louise. "I've got his number," said Leo, "I'll call him". He rummaged in his bag, pulled out his notebook and dialled the Priory on his cell-phone. The café was a little noisy so he went outside to engage in conversation with Marcus. He returned soon after saying; "Its fine with Marcus; he said we should go over as soon as we're ready and he'll make us lunch."

We went over to the Priory in Ruth's car. On the way I asked Leo about his experience. All he could say was that there was so much to think about that he didn't know where to start. The cave system itself was amazing; he wondered how far it extended, and were there any deeper levels. Also, he said; "let's not forget the lighting, what technology made that happen and how long had it been in operation; So many questions and no answers?" I think Leo was only vocalising what was going on in all of us, only he seemed more able to articulate his thoughts at the moment.

We arrived at the Priory about one o'clock. Brother Luke met us at the door and led us into the kitchen where Marcus, smiling as usual, was placing a large basket of bread rolls, fresh out of the oven if the smell was anything to go by, onto a large scrub-topped table. Places had been set around the table at which Marcus asked us to sit. I realised just how hungry I was as my mouth watered and my tummy rumbled. Marcus ladled out steaming bowls of home-made vegetable soup and we all tucked in. The taste of fenugreek cut right through the fog of tiredness that filled my mind and focussed my attention on the simple pleasure of enjoying good food. The bread rolls, mixed with rye flour, were indeed fresh out of the oven and tasted absolutely wonderful.

Insight and Resolution

"What happened yesterday?" asked Leo in a tired and frustrated voice. "That is a difficult question to answer without you being aware of several subjects, one of which is Psychometry," replied Marcus. Leo spoke earnestly, I had never seen him express his feelings so forcefully; "If it helps me understand what happened yesterday then please tell me what it is I need to know about Psychometry; I've never heard of it – what is it?" "That goes for me too," said Ruth and Louise in unison. I wanted to ask a whole lot of questions, but my mind was so befuddled through loss of sleep that all I could say was; "I second that" Marcus didn't say anything for a moment; he just looked at us quizzically. "The short answer", he began, "is that all things, be they animate or inanimate, have the ability to record events that occur within their field of experience, and Psychometry is the study of that particular ability and its mechanisms. In many ways it is the study of reading and creating memories and all that such implies." Ruth asked Marcus if this also applied to people. "Of course, it applies to all creatures, humanity included." "How is it possible to know that?" she exclaimed. "Because it is possible to read those memories; although to my way of thinking it is lamentable how few people are aware of it. However, with the right education it is possible to become reasonably proficient in reading such memories; that is what is meant by the term Psychometry."

Louise asked, "Are you saying everything, absolutely everything, including rocks and trees and things such as a mountain or a valley have memories?" "Yes" "Well I never," she said, "If you had told me that the day before yesterday I would never have believed you: In fact I'm not sure I believe you now!" "Is it a form of clairvoyance?" asked Ruth. "Yes, I suppose it is," replied Marcus, "Although it is probably more true to say that clairvoyance is a mode of psychometry – a mode of reading memories or impressions visually, as it were; although some people are able to hear things. For example, I knew a man who after moving into an old cottage occasionally heard church bells when he was working in his garden. He thought it was just the local church, but when in conversation with a local historian he discovered that the local church didn't have bells, and that it had never ever been furnished with bells, he was quite puzzled by it. Shortly after that discussion, and possibly even as a result of it, he visited the local library where he acquired a book on local history and discovered that his garden and the field beyond were on the site of a large monastery that had been destroyed during the reformation. He still hears the bells, and has since discovered a wide variety of archaeological remains from the monastery in and around his garden. However, his clairaudience is unusual; most people who develop psychometric abilities, at least at first, tune into them through touch. It's not so great a mystery as you might think; most people are sensitive to atmospheres, indeed the atmosphere of a place is no more than the general tone of the inherent memories. For example, when you enter someone's home you will gain through your sense of smell a general impression of the house. If there is food cooking that will contribute greatly to your overall impression. On the other hand, someone wearing perfume will often leave a trace of it long after they have left the room. It is more or less the same with memories in the sense that an

Insight and Resolution

impression of an event is made in the environment in which it occurred, and will remain for an indefinite period of time. How long that impression will remain is debatable, it all depends on the strength of the impression. Some argue that memories are retained permanently."

As he spoke I recalled a visit to the house in Amsterdam, where Anne Frank and her family had been concealed, hiding from the Nazis during World War II. The story is well known, and I had heard it many times, but the story is one thing whereas the atmosphere in that building was so overwhelmingly depressing that I had tears in my eyes as I wandered from room to room; I also heard sounds, memories if you will, that were made more than forty years previously. It was unforgettable. As I ruminated thus, I recalled on the same visit to Amsterdam, whilst exploring the streets around the old canal district, how on several occasions in the early evening I heard the sound of jack boots marching over the cobbled streets and even felt a wave of fear as they approached. One evening I thought I heard the faint sound of sirens synchronising with the sound of strutting jack boots. I never saw anything, but the experience made an immense impression on me. The memories, if that's what they were, had obviously made a very deep and lasting imprint on the soul of the city. I mentioned this to Marcus, who thought my experience a clear example of psychometry, and that I had probably tuned into the strongest memories of that area. He said, "Frequently, the strength of the memory is determined by the power of the impression. In the affairs of humanity that impression would be defined by the strength and quality of the emotion involved; the stronger the emotion the deeper and stronger the impression. Your experience in Amsterdam was arguably the strongest memories in its entire history."

Louise interrupted, saying, "I thought only living creatures retained memories!" Marcus replied; "All things are capable of retaining memories, however, it is generally only living creatures that are able to read them, and this is probably where your intuition is leading you, that is, to making the distinction between forming memories and reading them. Ruth joined in, exclaiming, "So you're saying that we were reading memories in the underground library, and that these memories were created by members of the Order you belong to, is that correct?" "Yes, I am saying that, sort of, but for you to understand the why's and wherefores, involved will take some doing." "Oh!" was all that Ruth could say. The look of amazement on her face was probably matched by all of us as we sat, dumbfounded, and confused.

Marcus then said, "Let me ask you all a question, what is intuition, what do you think it is? Don't answer immediately; think about it. I'm popping out for a couple of minutes; Brother Luke will make some coffee, meanwhile, think about my question, it is relevant to your situation." On that note Marcus left the kitchen and we were left sitting alone. We sat for a while lost in our own thoughts, then Ruth asked me what I thought intuition was, "I don't know for sure, a sixth sense, an instinct for the truth, something like that; but I'm certain it has a greater meaning than that." "Yes," replied Ruth, "I think you're right, what do you two think?" she said looking at Louise and Leo. Louise said hesitatingly, "I think it means direct knowledge…" "Yes it does,"

Insight and Resolution

interrupted Leo firmly, "that's exactly what it means. It comes from the Latin 'intuitio', which means to know directly, without having to rely on the senses." "Gosh!" was all I could say, "that's clever, where did you learn all that?" "I went to a Grammar school", he said sheepishly.

"He's quite right," said Marcus, entering the kitchen and sitting at the table. The word Intuition means to 'know' and to know directly as opposed to discursive reasoning which is based upon sensory experience. Over the last few weeks we have in various ways been discussing the difference between discursive thought and intuition. You might recall that in most of our discussions we have used the term 'mundane world', which describes the world of the senses and all that such implies. Discursive reasoning is rational thought based upon information gleaned from the world, from sensory data. Intuition, on the other hand, is knowledge gained directly without rational thought. We all have the faculty of Intuition, but most don't use it, except in very crude terms, where it is generally subject to the instinctive nature. In truth, except by reputation most of us don't even know it exists."

Brother Luke brought a pot of fresh coffee to the table. As he was serving the coffee, he said quietly, "I'm sorry to interrupt, but, if I may say, rather than sitting here in a state of bewilderment consider this: If you accept that you have an intuitive faculty, then how do you awaken and develop it; it's not as if it is a theoretical question is it? You have each experienced it to an advanced degree, have you not? So think, how do you develop the means of knowing directly, that is developing your intuitive faculty?" Leo sat up with a start. "Knowing directly, without recourse to the senses, means stepping outside of duality, by moving into a state of Unity, it has to be that way, no?" "You're moving in the right direction," commented Marcus, "But how do we step out of duality?" "Through self-knowledge acquired in meditation," said Louise. "Quite right, quite right," said Marcus. "Our awareness of Self is generally defined by our instinctive nature in the context of world experience, and under such circumstances we know of no other way than to think discursively; hence not only is our means of acquiring knowledge very limited, but the knowledge itself is only relative to the mundane world.

For example, we can observe how 'a' will follow 'b'; we don't have to know how or why, but experience teaches us it will happen, this is empirical knowledge – it is knowledge from observation only. Most of our lives are rooted in this mode of thinking, indeed, schools rarely take their pupils beyond. it We may also reason, using systems of logic to deduce or infer that something is or is not so. A good school or department of further education will introduce students to several methods of reasoning. However, as valuable as discursive reasoning may be, and it is valuable and not to be ignored, it only leads us to understand something of the world around us, the world of duality. It is not designed to function outside of a space-time context, that is to say, the mundane world. Alternatively, we may intuit." This was very interesting; I was beginning to understand what Marcus had been getting at over the past few weeks. "Yes," I said, "I think I understand what you mean. When you were talking about the Kabbalah over the last few weeks, you were introducing us to a

Insight and Resolution

model of consciousness, and how it functions at different levels. If I understand you right then the Nephesh signifies the soul as a reactive creature whose thinking is governed by what it observes in the mundane world, whereas the Ruach, signifies the soul led by reason..." "Yet," Interrupted Marcus, "whilst it is subject to the instinctive nature its reasoning powers and abilities merely serve that nature, it is a slave to biology." "I think I understand that now," I said, "you're saying that the Ruach can only engage in intuitive thought when it is emancipated from its bondage to biology."

It occurred to me that this was what the Kabbalah was really about, the emancipation of the soul from the instinctive nature. I said as much to Marcus. He said, "Essentially, you're right, the core teachings of the Kabbalah are a guide for the soul, leading it out of the lower worlds in much the same way as Ariadne's thread led Theseus out of the labyrinth." "I'm sorry to interrupt, " said Ruth "But what is Ariadne's thread?" "Oh! Well.." Marcus paused for a moment, "There is an ancient Greek myth about a great hero called Theseus, you can read about him in any book of Greek mythology, but the reference here is to the legend that once upon a time the city of Athens was forced to send a tribute every year of seven young men and women to Minos, the king of Crete. These young victims were given to the Minatour, a bestial creature, half human, half bull, confined in a deep and infinitely complex labyrinth of cave. He was so ferocious that none ever escaped him or got out of the labyrinth alive. The legend tells how Theseus volunteered to be one of the victims and went to Crete to destroy the Minatour. When he arrived he met and fell in love with

The Rose Priory Dialogues

Ariadne, the daughter of King Minos. The feeling was mutual, thus Ariadne assisted Theseus by providing him with a large ball of thread. Ariadne, standing at the entrance to the labyrinth, kept hold of one end of the thread whilst Theseus entered the labyrinth unwinding the thread as he went, thereby leaving a trail of fine thread so that he could find his way out when the time arrived. Eventually he confronted the monstrous Minatour and slew it, then retraced his path by following Ariadne's thread. Such is the legend.

To those schooled in the work, this story has a much deeper significance. Theseus is a type of Arjuna, an initiate, engaging in the work of overcoming his instinctive nature, and thereby emancipating the soul and all of its faculties. The point I was making is that the teachings of the Kabbalah are a kind of Ariadne's thread, a means of leading the soul through the labyrinth of the mundane world. Do you see now?" "Yes," said Louise, "But who is Ariadne?" "Ah!."Marcus paused, "That is an interesting question. More interesting than you might imagine. She was the daughter of king Minos, a son of Zeus, and his wife Pasiphae the daughter of Helios, the god of the Sun. Traditionally speaking the daughter of the Sun is the Moon, thus Ariadne is revealed as an aspect of the Moon, which is very closely connected to the real nature of the Labyrinth. So, you can see that this legend is something of an allegory concerning the emancipation, or if you will, the evolution of the soul. There is a great deal more to this story, but we digress. However, you could do a lot worse than spending some of your time studying the ancient myths."

Insight and Resolution

I listened to Marcus in wonder. I had instinctively known that there was much more to mythology than the often barren and prejudiced postulations of anthropologists and historians; this was great, I had been pointed towards something I could readily engage with, and, dare I say it, even enjoy. From a very early age I had derived great pleasure from myths and legends about distant times and far-away places in worlds that had long since disappeared, of great heroes undertaking impossible tasks and winning against insurmountable odds – great stuff or what! As I mused thus I heard Ruth asking Marcus how we might develop our intuitive faculty. This drew my attention back to the issues at hand, why we were at the Priory. He didn't answer immediately, I could see he was pondering the question. After a while he said, "A couple of weeks ago we were discussing the chemistry of consciousness, particularly the nature of thought-forms, how they consist of images, feelings and the intellectual constructs we call thoughts. The environment in which this chemistry takes place is the mind, that much is obvious, indeed our comprehension of thought-forms and mind is generally synonymous, and we normally attribute the brain, or our head, as being the physical location of the mind and its activities. However, I was taught, and I offer it to you for your own consideration, that the real environment of the mind is a field of energy encasing the physical body whose shape appears to those who can see it in the form of an egg; we call it the 'Sphere of Sensation'. Within it dance the thought forms that you usually believe is taking place in your brain. Understanding this sphere and your relationship to it is of critical importance.

The Rose Priory Dialogues

For the majority of us the thought forms prevailing within this sphere are normally generated by our biology – which is geared to fulfilling the basic instincts of survival and procreation. We consider biology to be the very stuff of our being; but it isn't, and we must understand the distinction before we can make progress in self-knowledge. Furthermore, we must realise that the Self is not the thought-form either, and without understanding these two points, that Self is neither biology, nor thought-form, we will never learn to distinguish between intuitive and discursive knowledge. In the precincts of the sanctuary it is taught that God and angels know directly, that is to say intuitively, what men clumsily achieve by reasoning; this is because the soul, dwelling in the divine presence shares in that intuitive state. It is only when separated from that presence – in the space-time environment we call duality – that the soul is subjected to the need to work things out via discursive means. it is, then, with good reason that in western culture the path of spiritual development has traditionally consisted of two parts, the preparatory or Outer Work and the more advanced Inner Work. However, it is my conviction that both parts are equally difficult and profound.

The Outer Work consist of the rites of Purification and Elevation. Purification is the labourious process of separating the Will from the controlling influence of the lower or instinctive nature – our biology. Elevation is accomplished by refining the Will through spiritual disciplines and raising the emerging consciousness through and beyond the discursive mind. The Inner Work consists of Sacrifice and Consecration. Sacrifice is the surrendering of the purified Will to the Lord. It is a labour of love undertaken either in the sanctuary or in the world; it matters little what environment is chosen: the choice will be a matter of inspired vocation. Consecration is the transformation of the purified Human Will in its union or Celestial marriage with the Lord Jesus Christ. As I have mentioned previously, any soul undertaking this work must first learn to distinguish between Self and biology, between the chemist and the chemistry. Initially the student must learn to observe the chemistry at work. This takes time as students spend many hours in meditation observing their interior life and learning how their idea of 'self' is conditioned by the chemistry therein. At some point the student will eventually make the distinction. It is not an intellectual distinction, but a substantive knowing – a true intuition. It is the beginning of self-knowledge."

"But what then", I asked, "What happens when one has made the distinction between Self and biology?" "That, my young friend is the begging question, what indeed do you do? Well, let me put it this way, the spiritual philosophers of the ancient world recognised intuition to be a function of the highest part of the human intellect, the Nous, as distinct from the fleeting impressions of the senses upon the lower mental processes. The soul that has withdrawn from the things of the world, having turned within, must of necessity ascend, as Plotinus put it, towards the Good, the desired of all. I use the term the Divine Presence to signify the same thing; it is of God and lies beyond all dualities, beyond all form, in truth it is indescribable. However, there is a considerable amount of work to do before that can happen, indeed, the Outer Worker generally takes a very long time, years, decades, even longer."

The Rose Priory Dialogues

"But what has any of this to do with what happened in the tower?" asked Louise. "Be patient my friend, we'll get there eventually," replied Marcus. "Over the course of centuries members of this Order have spent countless years meditating on the nature of existence and the spiritual truths underpinning that existence. Their meditations were never simply intellectual reflections, but the full application of the chemistry of consciousness applied to the development of thought-forms relevant to the object of their meditation. Not infrequently these meditations would last for months. Thus, from the earliest times each and every member of the Order has contributed to the development of thought-forms that constitute the memories you experienced in the Library. To the contemplative it not the thought-form that is significant but the understanding derived from it. Your experience therein was caused by such thought-forms acting on your individual psyches, rather than the prevailing influence of the mundane world that constitutes your normal everyday experience. Indeed, you experienced but a tiny fraction of the memories contained in the Hall of Records that we call the library."

"Is what you call the library the Akasic Records?" asked Leo. "What are Akasic Records?" said Ruth before Marcus could answer. "I think," continued Leo, "they are the memories or records of all that has ever happened, including all human experience, held in a universal memory bank, sort of thing." "Does such a thing actually exist?" asked Louise in a challenging sort of way. We all looked at Marcus. "Where do I start? Leo is more or less right, but there's a lot more to it. The term Akasic Records is a

Insight and Resolution

European interpretation of an ancient Hindu concept concerning the nature of the fifth element Akasa, which is a sanskrit word signifying the element Ether. It is an invisible medium wherein all things formed have their existence. The term became popular among members of the Theosophical Society in the latter part of the nineteenth century and has since become a commom-place in certain stratas of popular culture. The most significant feature of this concept is that the Akasic Records contain the memories of all events that have ever taken place in creation, and that they are readily available to any who know how to access them."

I asked Marcus what he meant by the fifth element, and what Akasa was as I hadn't really understood his words. He informed us that in Hindu cosmology there are five elements Prithvi – earth, Vayu – air, Jala – water, Agni – fire, all of which were created from the fifth element Akasa – ether. This ether, he added, wasn't the gaseous ether of modern chemistry, but a pure primary matter that to all intents and purposes is invisible and unknowable to the senses. It isn't so different in western thought, which proposes four elements only – earth, air, fire and water; ether is not considered to be an element proper, but a medium in which the four elements exist. Marcus then added, "The concept of a universal medium is not unique to any one culture, and has been a subject of immense speculation over the centuries. So, without losing ourselves in the whys and wherefores of this complex subject I suggest that you accept for the moment that such records do exist in much the same way as our own individual memories exist. How we understand and work with the phenomenon is a matter of tradition, of which a great deal of material has been passed on from one generation to the other.

Do you remember our discussion a few weeks ago, where we explored the subject of the group mind?" We all nodded simultaneously, although none of us were able to articulate a response. Marcus continued, "The great ocean of life, known in some schools as the World-Soul, in which we all have our existence, may also be thought of as the group mind of life. Within it every species has its own unique group mind. In the group mind of humanity exist many sub groups consisting of races, nations, religions, languages, political affiliations etc. Most of us belong to several group minds at the same time, and every one of us contributes to the group minds to which we belong, and in turn are influenced and shaped by them. All of these groups have accumulated, and continue to accumulate, unique memories of their experiences, and all contribute to the memory bank of the World-Soul, developing what might be called Akasic records. It is relatively easy to access your own memories, and perhaps the memories of the group-minds you belong to, but accessing the memories of others, or of alien groups-minds is conditional and fraught with difficulties.

What you experienced in the tower were thought-forms built up over years by members of the Order. You could say that they were memories of the group-mind of the Order, but that would be misleading. It would be more correct to say that they are expressions or reflections of spiritual archetypes within the group-mind of the Order. If you recall, Plotinus, taught three principal modes or states called 'Hypostases'. The first he defines

Insight and Resolution

as The One, the prime source and principle of all being. The second the Divine Nous or Divine Mind, in which exist the archetypal ideas and prototypes of all Creation. The third, proceeding from the Divine Nous, is the World Soul. Human souls proceed from the World Soul, and like the World Soul may also be subdivided to reflect the principles of the Hypostases as Spirit, Soul and Body. It is a fundamental part of the Order teaching that through the highest intellect in man it is possible to contemplate the archetypal ideas and prototypes that are manifest in creation; thus, members of the Order have long contemplated the archetypal world, and you were privileged to share in their experience."

As I listened to Marcus I recalled reading somewhere that the alchemists of old worked extensively with the elements, particularly ether. I asked Marcus if he knew anything about that, and if it was actually relevant to our discussion. He grinned at me, and informed us that Alchemy is a vast subject more labyrinthine than that constructed to hold the Minatour. "However, It may be said with some degree of certainty that Alchemy, as practised in western civilisation, has come down to us through the Arabs, who, probably received it from the Greeks and the Egyptians. According to Zosimus of Panopolis, an alchemist of the late third century, alchemy was a secret art practised in Egypt under the close supervision of its pharaoh and priesthood, and that this art was taught exclusively by oral transmission. From the earliest times the term has been applied to the art of metallurgy, particular in the area of transforming metals and the formation of alloys. It has also been used as a term to describe the art of drawing out the essences of material substances, be they metal, mineral or vegetable. However, in Europe, from the beginning of the eleventh century to the present day, alchemy has increasingly denoted either a physical or spiritual art or science. Frequently the two have overlapped in confusing ways.

The common and least critical opinion concerning Alchemy is that it was the primitive forerunner of modern chemistry. Others have described it as little more than a pseudo-science that emerged in the middle of the first millennium, and whose objective was the conversion of common metals into silver and gold by means of a fabulous agent called the Philosopher's Stone, and that its devotees were either knaves or fools whose objectives were entirely mercenary or delusory. It is an opinion not entirely without foundation as during the course of its history Alchemy has certainly proved attractive to both knave and fool. However, there is another opinion, an opinion shared by those few who see it as a spiritual science whose discourses and tractates are veiled in allegory and metaphor, and whose objectives have little regard for material objectives and ambitions. It is an opinion that I share in principle.

In my understanding the word 'alchemy' is derived from the Greek word 'Chymia' which means 'to flow, or, to draw/pour out.' It probably acquired this name in the city of Alexandria, a place where many ancient disciplines converged to be re-defined in the Greco-Roman world, before it passed into the emerging civilisation of the Arabs. Whatever the true etymology may be, it suggests a divine science or teaching concerning spiritual regeneration. The alchemist conceives the universe to be a unity; that all material bodies evolved from one seed; their component

Insight and Resolution

elements being merely different forms of one matter and, therefore convertible into one another. This theory may be seen as an analogy concerning the mystical doctrine of the soul's evolution and regeneration – an evolution from an unregenerate state symbolised by Lead to a spiritually regenerate state symbolised by Gold.

Alchemy also assumes the existence of three principles in all things, corresponding with the threefold division of man into body, soul and spirit. In alchemical terms these principles are Mercury, Sulphur, and Salt. Do not make the mistake of confusing these principles with the material substances that go by the same names, but understand that from an alchemical perspective the manifestation of creation takes place through the agency of three spiritual principles acting in conjunction with each other, and that different cultures have given them different names.

In the western tradition, and I describe them in no particular order of precedence, Sulphur represents the masculine principle – the Spiritus Primus. Its nature is fire, and is understood to be the analogue of the soul. Some alchemists have postulated two sulphurs, an inner and an outer. The outer is thought to be the cause of all impurity. The inner, on the other hand, was regarded as pure, and essential to the evolution of the metals: thus it is taught that pure mercury matured by a pure inward sulphur yields pure gold. To Sulphur is attributed the Sun, the conscious self – the embodiment of will. Mercury represents the feminine principle – the Materia Prima. Its nature is water, which in alchemy is understood to be the Spirit. This is not the spirit of Christian theology, which denotes the divine immortal element of Man, but the vital force that is carried in the air, otherwise called the 'waters of life'. It is passive malleable and volatile; to it is attributed the Moon. Salt represents the Body, the material form resulting from the combination of Mercury and Sulphur.

These three principles, acting together, constitute not only the nature of metal but of all things, including man. Thus, Gold is the symbol of regeneration, and is designated a noble metal; as is Silver, although it is thought to be less mature than gold. Emanuel Swedenborg, the Eighteenth century renowned Swedish scientist, philosopher and spiritual visionary, following the ancient tradition, designated the man of gold as "celestial", and the man of Silver as "spiritual". Lead, on the other hand, was regarded as a very immature and impure metal: heavy and dull, and as such was considered to be a symbol of man in a sinful and unregenerate condition.

From another perspective, a perspective that lies closer to the heart of the Order, Sulphur, as Primus Spiritus, corresponds with the Divine Nous, whilst Quicksilver, as Materia Prima, corresponds with the World Soul. It is through the conjunction of them both, symbolised by the alchemical marriage of the King and Queen, that the World Soul gives form to the archetypes contained in potentia within the Divine Nous. The materialised forms of the archetypes, and all forms derived from them are represented by the element of salt.

Furthermore, the chemistry of consciousness, to which I am continually directing your attention, is an expression of this spiritual alchemy within the human psyche. It has many layers, and they do not reveal themselves readily. The work of an initiate

Insight and Resolution

is a labour in Self-knowledge, an endeavour that requires of us that we understand our nature and the chemistry of consciousness that is a fundamental part of it. When we understand how it works we can then use it to good effect in the Magnum Opus." Ruth said, "I am beginning to make sense of this now, In some ways it's all about language, isn't it; but, 'Magnum Opus' I've come across the phrase before, but what does it mean?" Marcus considered the question and looked at us all, "The words Magnum Opus, means simply the 'Great Work'. The real question is what is the Great Work? In many walks of life it refers to the completion of a life-time of labour, perhaps a composer's final and greatest creation, or perhaps an artist's defining piece of work. However, in alchemical terms it is the creation of the Philosophers Stone, a wondrous stone that had the power to transform lead into gold. Many people have sought it, seeking to create a real physical stone that has the power to transform Lead into Gold. Such people have long been called in disparaging terms, 'Puffers', from their incessant search for a physical stone. As I said earlier, alchemy has attracted many knaves and fools to its workshops. Nevertheless, from the Order's perspective our Lead is human nature and our Gold is human nature spiritualised; by which I mean the full realisation of the divine potential that lies at the heart of the soul. Our workshop is the soul, in which the divine marriage of Sulphur and Mercury is forever taking place."

I asked Marcus why he had introduced us to the Tower, and showed us those particular thought-forms. He said, "I gave you a gift, a series of memories that may serve as the basis of fruitful meditations. Think of them, if you will, as seeds that if nurtured carefully will grow into beautiful forms full of meaning and rich in spiritual wisdom. It is unlikely you will forget them, even if most fade from your memory, one or more will stay with you and inspire you to engage in meditation." With that said. Marcus suggested that instead of pressing for more answers and overloading our minds with more information, we should reflect upon what we have learned so far, and if we are so inclined attend the evening offices once or twice a week as many of our anxieties would be washed away in the spiritual light generated therein by our devotions. Thus we sat chatting for several hours, sometimes seriously sometimes not; Marcus let me copy his recipe for the soup and the bread rolls we had for lunch; Ruth and Louise took a walk around the grounds with brother Luke, and Leo went in search of the Chapel. Eventually the evening started to draw in and we all joined the brothers and sisters of the Order for the Evening Office, which proved to be the beginning of an incredible journey; the narration of which must wait for another time.

Epilogue

Joseph spent many months attending the daily Offices at the
Rose Priory before eventually taking his vows as a brother of the
Order of St. Denys. On one of his visits he informed me that at
the close of the millennium he had been ordained to the
priesthood and now spends much of his time travelling between
the various chapter-houses of the Order - a more extraordinary
undertaking than one might at first imagine; as I discovered
upon reading his second manuscript.